Perceptions

Perceptions of great engineers: fact and fantasy

Proceedings of a one-day conference held at the Merseyside Maritime Museum, Liverpool, on 26 June 1993

edited by Denis Smith

Science Museum for
the Newcomen Society,
National Museums and Galleries on Merseyside and
the University of Liverpool

Published 1994

British Library Cataloguing-in-Publication Data
A catalogue record for this publication is available
from the British Library

Set from Pagemaker in Postscript Monotype Plantin Light.
Printed in Great Britain by Antony Rowe Ltd, Chippenham, Wiltshire

ISBN 0 901805 65 3

Science Museum, Exhibition Road, London SW7 2DD, UK
Newcomen Society, Exhibition Road, London SW7 2DD, UK
National Museums and Galleries on Merseyside, Liverpool L3 4AA, UK
The University of Liverpool, Liverpool L69 3BX, UK

Contents

List of contributors

Denis Smith	Chartered engineer, historian of technology, extra-mural lecturer at London University, and Vice-President of the Newcomen Society, London
D J Bryden	Keeper, Department of Science, Technology and Working Life in the National Museums of Scotland, Edinburgh
Hugh Torrens	Lecturer, Department of Geology, Keele University
Adrian Jarvis	Curator, Port History, Merseyside Maritime Museum, Liverpool
Simon Dentith	Reader in English, Cheltenham and Gloucester College of Higher Education
Victoria Haworth	Director of the Robert Stephenson Trust, Newcastle upon Tyne
Mary Murphy	Archivist, and Secretary to the Panel for Historical Engineering Works, Institution of Civil Engineers, London
James L Wood	Keeper, Department of Science, Technology and Working Life in the National Museums of Scotland, Edinburgh (now retired)
M C Duffy	Lecturer, School of Engineering & Advanced Technology, University of Sunderland

Introduction

Denis Smith

This volume comprises a series of papers presented at a one-day conference held at the Merseyside Maritime Museum, Albert Dock, Liverpool, in June 1993. The meeting was the result of collaboration between the National Museums and Galleries on Merseyside, the University of Liverpool and the Newcomen Society for the Study of the History of Engineering and Technology, founded in 1920.

The model for engineering biography which was to develop in the United Kingdom was established in the middle of last century by Samuel Smiles. It began with his work on *George Stephenson* (1857), followed by three volumes of *Lives of the Engineers* (1862), and *Boulton and Watt* (1865). He was a pioneer, and in the preface to the first volume of *Lives of the Engineers* he said, 'Notwithstanding the national interest which might be supposed to belong to this branch of literature, it has hitherto received but little attention.' The only precedents for his work were modest entries in encyclopaedias and biographical dictionaries. His work on the engineers was influenced by the thesis he produced in his first successful work, *Self-Help*, published in 1859. He dealt not only with such distinguished engineers as James Brindley, John Smeaton, John Rennie, and George and Robert Stephenson but was keen to include 'several meritorious though now all but forgotten persons, who are entitled to notice as amongst the pioneers of English engineering'. It is easy to see that Smiles regarded the rise of the engineer from craftsman to designer as a good example of his philosophy of self-help. Just one page of his preface contains such revealing words as 'heroic', 'dramatic', 'noble', 'skilled', 'strong-minded', 'resolute' and 'ingenious'. Nevertheless, he was thorough in his work on documents, and of course he had unique access to living prime sources.

There has been a steady, if sparse, flow of volumes of engineering biography — about three a decade since Smiles' death in 1904. There have been periods of interesting activity in this century. First, there were the excellent books by three pioneers of the Newcomen Society, namely: *James Watt and the Steam Engine* (H W Dickinson and Rhys Jenkins, 1927), *Richard Trevithick: The Engineer and the Man* (H W Dickinson and A Titley, 1934), *James Watt: Craftsman and Engineer* (H W Dickinson, 1935) and *Matthew Boulton* (H W Dickinson, 1936). These became standard works for nearly a generation. Twenty years later these were followed by a superb trilogy of biographies by L T C Rolt: *Isambard Kingdom Brunel* (1957), *Thomas Telford* (1958) and *George and Robert Stephenson* (1960). These reached a very wide public and did a great deal to raise public awareness of the nature of engineering and of the men who engaged in it. Rolt, writing in the preface to the first of the trilogy, said:

> Much has been written about this Industrial Revolution, as we call it, but the effect of most of this writing is curiously impersonal and therefore unreal. It is as though the Revolution was the product of some *deus ex machina* or of some corporate act of will on the part of a whole people . . . if the fathers of the Revolution are mentioned at all they appear only as shadows.[1]

In 1960 he added:

> My object in undertaking this biographical trilogy was not to add anything to this general historical picture, but to attempt to correct its bias by trying to breathe some life into a few of the most important of these leaders and put them in the foreground where they properly belong.[2]

There can be no doubt that Rolt achieved this. It is significant, however, that Rolt's new work was confined to engineers with whom Smiles had dealt a century earlier.

However, the time has arrived to take a fresh look at the subject of engineering biography, and the aim of these conference papers, arranged in more-or-less chronological order, is to examine in detail two historiographical problems: first, the selection of engineers for immortalisation (which has remained remarkably unanimous since the work of Samuel Smiles), and second, the accumulation, within engineering biography, of a folk tradition which has affected scholarly works as well as popular history. The title of this volume raises several issues: what personal characteristics and achievements constitute a *great* engineer? Why were some engineers selected for reverential biography whilst others were virtually ignored? The subtitle, *Fact and Fantasy*, promises a questioning of the tradition of engineering biography and a revisionist approach to the subject. In engineering biography it is often difficult to strike the balance between exploring the character of the man himself and a description of his works. In most cases it is not too difficult to find the technical details of structures and machines from published reports, surviving drawings or even the artefacts themselves. It is always easier to establish *how* rather than *why* a particular problem was solved in one way rather than another. Diaries and letters usually reveal more of the writer's personality, although an engineer under pressure when giving evidence to a Parliamentary Committee often revealed his character and temperament in a striking way. However, there is a wide disparity in surviving source material between engineers. The several authors here draw on a remarkable range of sources to provide insights into these fascinating problems.

David Bryden argues that James Watt's early years in Glasgow have been overshadowed by the subsequent success of the steam engine and throws new light on his activities as instrument-maker, investor, surveyor and civil engineer. Hugh Torrens examines the extent to which Jonathan Hornblower's reputation was deliberately undermined in order to magnify the achievement of Watt. Adrian Jarvis describes the way in which successive biographies of George Stephenson have become less, rather than more, accurate, whilst Simon Dentith shows that some engineering biographies can be identified as mythological purely by their literary style.

Victoria Haworth re-assesses the respective roles of Robert Stephenson, Joseph Locke, John Stephenson and John Rastrick. Mary Murphy, as Archivist to the Institution of Civil Engineers, is uniquely placed to reveal something of the newly acquired Mackenzie collection of papers — the greatest nineteenth-century engineering archive source to emerge this century. The collection is all the more important in that it deals with that under-represented body, the civil engineering contractors.

James Wood explores a case where the heroic, 'great man' approach to engineering biography has caused those who submerge their identity in teamwork to be forgotten. Finally, Michael Duffy suggests that engineering biography has been adversely affected by a failure to set its subject in a philosophical context.

Altogether this is a series of papers which, it is hoped, will stimulate reaction and promote further discussion on the aims, methods and subjects of engineering biography, past, present and future.

I would like to acknowledge my gratitude to Mr D H W Hayton for his expert assistance during the electronic stage of editing these papers.

Notes and references

1 Rolt, L T C, 'Preface', *Isambard Kingdom Brunel* (London: Pelican, 1957), p13

2 Rolt, L T C, 'Preface', *George and Robert Stephenson, the Railway Revolution* (London: Pelican, 1978), pxii

James Watt, merchant: the Glasgow years, 1754–1774

D J Bryden

Early this century, Andrew Carnegie commented on the story of 13-year-old James Watt being criticised by his aunt for wasting time playing with a boiling kettle:

> To what extent the precocious boy ruminated upon the phenomenon must be left to conjecture. Enough that the story has a solid foundation upon which we can build. This more than justifies us in classing it with 'Newton and the Apple', 'Bruce and the Spider', 'Tell and the Apple', 'Galvani and the Frog', 'Volta and the damp Cloth', 'Washington and his Little Hatchet' — a string of gems, almost the most precious of our legendary possessions. Let no rude iconoclast attempt to undermine one of them. *Even if they never occurred it matters little. They should have occurred, for they are too good to lose.* We could part with many of the actual characters of the flesh in history without much loss; banish the imaginary host of the spirit, and we were poor indeed. *So with these inspiring legends; let us accept them and add others gladly as they arise, inquiring not too curiously into their origin.*[1] [my emphasis]

As a teenager who emigrated from Scotland in 1848, Carnegie was and is a prime exemplar of one who seized the opportunities offered by the New World. The Pittsburg telegraph boy became the foremost ironmaster in the United States, and devoted the last two decades of his life to a philanthropy that provided a material underpinning to the popular doctrines of self-help,[2] propounded by his countryman Samuel Smiles. Theirs was an ethic which repeated, thrived on and, if necessary, created the 'inspiring legend' that became the stuff of popular history. What is at issue is not the fact that overtly hagiographic and partial Victorian biographies of the great engineers have cast long shadows on the public imagination, but the insidious and persistent influence on generations of those who have written histories of eighteenth- and nineteenth-century British technology.[3] Long-lasting and potent stories, however ill founded, are certainly informative about how participants wished to be remembered by their contemporaries, and how later generations, in expressing their view of the past, saw their own present. The life-cycle of such accounts are worthy of study in their own right, but historians must be sophisticated in their evaluation of such evidence, so as to ensure that use clarifies rather than obscures the history of the period.

Accounts of the 20 years that Watt spent working in Glasgow have been overshadowed by the subsequent success of the steam engines designed, made and marketed by Boulton and Watt in Birmingham. As if to emphasise the inevitable glory of what was to follow, accounts of Watt's Glasgow years highlight only those matters that are seen as preludes to the inexorable triumph of the separate condenser. They largely understate, ignore or belittle his other activities. For well over a century historians have, with gratitude, mined the collection of Watt's correspondence published by J P Muirhead in 1854, but the editor's 'introductory memoir' implicitly indicates the selective nature of the volumes.[4] This paper does not set out to challenge the notion of Watt as an engineer of singular genius. It does not question the importance of the technical innovations that he brought to the design of the steam engine, nor doubt the related importance of Matthew Boulton's entrepreneurial skills. Rather it attempts to balance existing biographical accounts, by drawing attention to the richness of Watt's other activities in Glasgow.

As instrument-maker, investor, surveyor and civil engineer, Watt was active at a critical time in the growth of industrial activity in Scotland. His specific activities provide further evidence of that development in the decades following the Jacobite rising of 1745. Specifically, their recounting needs to be seen in the context of industrial development in lowland Scotland, and should ensure that evaluation of Watt's Glasgow years is well founded, rather than being merely the background to an account that is all too often warped by the infectious enthusiasm for steam that Boulton did so much to encourage.

James Watt: instrument-maker

James Watt spent a year learning the instrument-making trade in Glasgow before setting out in June 1755 to enhance his skills by working for a mathematical instrument-maker in London.[5] It was a sensible move, for London was then the leading European centre for the manufacture of instruments.[6] Those early commentators who refer to this period did not credit Watt's first master as having any great skills. The earliest commentator, writing shortly after Watt had retired from business in 1800, had an explicit appreciation of the fact that the trade of instrument making outside London was then quite different from the renowned trade in the metropolis. The young man was then apprenticed in a profession which

> included the making and repairing of the instruments made use of in experiments in mechanics and natural philosophy; the manufacture in a rough way, of all kinds of musical instruments, and of theodolites, quadrants, and other instruments necessary for the practice of land surveying.[7]

Subsequent commentators embroidered the position. Thus having set up in business in Glasgow, Watt's activities were reported as covering

> making and repairing the instruments used in the experiments in mechanics and natural philosophy, and those used in surveying; but also the manufacture, in a rough way, of all kinds of musical instruments; drawing lines on dials; cleaning and repairing wooden clocks, making and repairing fishing-tackle; and acting as a general sort of rough cutler; . . . but the greater part of his time was taken up in making and repairing drawing pens, compasses, and plotting scales, and making balances and weights.[8]

To the nineteenth-century reader, this description made an implicit contrast with the London trade, where mathematical, philosophical and optical instruments were manufactured in whole or in part largely by sub-contracting specialists, with musical instruments, scales and weights, and fishing tackle being made and sold by quite distinct groups of tradesmen. Indeed, Watt himself soon discovered that, such was the division of labour in the London trade in 1755, he was fortunate to find a teacher with a broad repertoire of skills.[9]

For the early biographers, it was the low level of the skills of Watt's Glasgow master that sent him to London. Their hero could be taught little by a rude mechanic

> who eked out a scanty subsistence by making and repairing fishing tackle and the simple instruments used in mechanical drawing. By turns a cutler and a white smith, a repairer of fiddles and a tuner of spinets, a useful man at almost everything. He retailed knicknacks of many kinds and through dealing in spectacles was dignified with the title of optician.[10]

Such a description invites a contrast between the multifarious penny-grubbing activities of the mentor with the sublime attainments of his erstwhile pupil. It is, however, a judgemental view of Watt's early years in Glasgow. It suggests a poverty of achievement by the provincial master in stark contrast with the manifest accomplishments which his illustrious apprentice will attain. Regrettably, such an account obscures the rich background to the development of mechanical skills and industrialisation in mid-eighteenth-century Scotland. When this story is further embroidered to describe Watt as 'handy at dressing trout and salmon flies', literary fancy has submerged fact.[11]

The name of Watt's first master is currently unknown. There were at least two men working in Glasgow to whom he could have been indentured: Henry Drew and George Jarden. Drew from 1730 and Jarden from 1738 acted as laboratory stewards to successive professors of natural philosophy in the University of Glasgow.[12] Both men were metal workers, members of the Incorporation of Hammermen, with special competence in horological work.[13]

One of Watt's earliest jobs as an instrument-maker came from the University of Glasgow. In October 1756, newly returned from London, he was asked to unpack and clean the bequest of astronomical instruments recently arrived from Jamaica.[14] After spending the first half of 1757 working as an instrument-maker in his home town of Greenock, Watt moved to Glasgow in August. Quite where he was located is uncertain — but by December he had begun to trade from a workshop in the College.[15] The precedent for support to trades relevant to general academic endeavour had been created by the printers J and A Foulis and the typefounder Alexander Wilson.[16] The association with the University was explained by James Cleland in 1820:

> As the making of Philosophical Instruments was but little known in Scotland at that time, several of the Professors, from desire to patronize that art, requested his acceptance of the use of three apartments within the College, for carrying on his business, adjoining to those used by Messers Foulis, Printers.[17]

It is indeed the case that scientific instrument manufacture was little known in Scotland in the 1750s, although an English craftsman had brought the trade to Edinburgh in the late 1640s.[18] Having a craftsman with Watt's skills based in the College had advantages for the professoriate. There was the potential requirement to assist with the new astronomical instruments being acquired for the proposed observatory, further work on the MacFarlane bequest, plus the routine maintenance of the apparatus used in teaching natural philosophy and chemistry. Watt retained a presence in the University for some years, but had a shop in the town by late 1759, initially in Saltmarket, moving to the Trongate in December 1763.[19]

The first myth about Watt's Glasgow activities grew from the early location of his business in the College — the claim that local craftsmen attempted to stop the youngster trading in the town:

> Mr Watt came to settle in Glasgow, as a maker of Mathematical Instruments; but being molested by some of the corporations who considered him as an intruder on their privileges, the University protected him by giving him a shop within their precincts, and by conferring on him the title of Mathematical Instrument maker to the University.[20]

This statement appears in the first paragraph of the testimony of the eminent chemist, Joseph Black, writing in 1796 in support of Boulton, Watt & Sons in their litigation against engineers accused of infringing Watt's patents. Biographers have repeated the claim, some adding to the myth through their comments: Samuel Smiles refers to 'the incubus of the guilds'; J P Muirhead to 'tradesmen of more arrogant and far more unfounded pretensions than the modest youth whom they persecuted'; an anonymous English reviewer of one early account sourly recorded 'the affected adulation of his countrymen, who now plume themselves with his merits, though at first they refused him even a locality for a humble shop'.[21] Although H Lumsden demonstrated in 1911 that there was no evidence whatsoever from the records of the Incorporation of Hammermen, or the Dean of Guild Court, that Watt had been targeted for exclusion,[22] the tale continued to be retold with more or less circumspection. It is the case that the Glasgow Dean of Guild Court did sporadically issue notices warning those who had established 'shops, ware-houses and cellars and trading under different denominations without having been properly entered Burgess and paid the fines to entitle them to a free trade within the Burgh . . . ' to purchase their Burgess tickets, or be fined and have their premises locked against them.[23] Despite the requirement, Watt traded as an instrument-maker, hiring journeymen and booking his own apprentices from the very start of business. The fact of Watt's subsequent fame and the repetition of Black's accusation of 'molestation' by the incorporations, was sufficient for a historian of the University to allow the institution to bathe in reflected glory for having given 'recognition and assistance to struggling merit'.[24] Opposition of the trade incorporations cannot be maintained. Furthermore, Watt could have purchased a Burgess ticket at any time by paying the fee demanded of a stranger — indeed, and this was overlooked by Lumsden, he became a Burgess and Guild Brother in March 1768, claiming the right through his father-in-law.[25]

After a year in business Watt was wondering about diversification, unsure whether Glasgow could provide him with sufficient business:

> unless it be the Hadley's instrument [i.e. the navigator's reflecting octant] there is nothing to be got by it, as at most other jobs I am obliged to do most of them myself, and as it is impossible for one person to be expert at everything, they often cost me more time than they should do . . . I and one lad finish three in a week easily; and selling them at 28s 6d, which is vastly below what they were ever sold at before, I have 40s clear on the three . . . If that does not succeed, I must fall into some other way of business, as this will not do in its present situation.[26]

Even at this early date, it is noteworthy that Watt had help from a 'lad' — indeed his own records show him taking on workmen on short-term contracts from May 1757.[27]

From the records of sales, income and expenditure recorded in an incomplete series of *Waste Books, Cash Books* and *Ledgers,* plus detailed payments to employees recorded in *Journeymen Books,* the growth in activities of the workshop can be closely followed. Efforts to sell octants certainly loom large in the early years, with parcels being sent for retail to Bristol, Port Glasgow and Greenock, to shops in Glasgow itself, with a dozen instruments even being sent to the West Indies. On the manufacturing side, the specialisation of journeymen employed on piece rates can be seen — in 1761, for example, Alexander Gardner did glass grinding, Robert Allen made and mended guitars and violins, and John Gardner, a man of Watt's own age taken on as an apprentice in 1760, was charging his master 2s 6d a week for providing 'bed, bord and washen of Morrey Osborn', the junior apprentice.[28] Watt's biographers make much of the mathematical instrument-maker (though himself tone deaf) turning his skills to the manufacture of musical instruments.[29] The business records suggest that the real skill was that of a workshop manager; since during the early 1760s Watt's employees included men who were primarily musical instrument-makers.[30] Flutes, violins and guitars were sent to retailers in London, Edinburgh and Dublin. Indeed, such was Watt's ability to organise the manufacture of musical instruments that in 1766 Charles Claggett invited Watt to become a partner in his Dublin business.[31] Either to provide his own customers with a range of goods, or in order to generate income from retailing, Watt himself purchased wholesale from sources in London, Birmingham and Sheffield. Workshop tools were purchased from John Wyke in Liverpool, glass barometer tubes from Newcastle, boxwood from London. Parcels of 'sundrie goods' were shipped for retail to Exeter, Shrewsbury and Perth, and even as far afield as a Scotch merchant in Quebec; musical instruments were sent for retail to London, Edinburgh and Dublin.[32] During the later part of the 1760s over half of the turnover of the business appears to have been retailing cutlery, other household ironmongery, toiletries and similar 'toys', with musical and scientific instruments accounting for about 15 and 30 per cent of sales respectively.[33]

The documentary evidence is quite clear. Watt the instrument-maker does not fit a stereotype of a dedicated craftsman beavering away in a small workshop, aided only by a young apprentice. Watt was clearly a business man with vision, taking on employees and trainees, buying in a broad range of merchandise to realise his ambition of significant commercial success. It was presumably to assist expansion of the business that he entered into partnership with an established Glasgow merchant, John Craig. Formally instituted in late 1759, each man had a half share in the stock (£69), tools (£23) and cash (£108).[34] The cash was presumably largely Craig's investment, an addition to small sums that Watt had borrowed in 1757 and 1758.[35] The further cash injections made by Craig from time to time are given on an annual basis: 1760, £88; 1761, £150; 1762, £108; 1763, £171 (of which £159 borrowed by 22 August); and 1764, £183.[36]

Watt drew an annual salary from the partnership of £35. Craig's investment was not on the basis of a share in the profits, but risk free, with interest to be paid on loans advanced. Only one interest payment was made prior to the settlement of the loan.[37] Watt used his detailed records of income and expenditure to create secondary records which balanced annual outgoings against annual income. However, in these balances he failed, for example, to carry forward liabilities such as interest due on loans. Superficial reading of the available records for the period up to and including 1764 suggests that without Craig's support the business would have been insolvent, but that is currently only a hypothesis. The records are incomplete and Watt's summaries may have been designed to show only that his income covered his outgoings.

By the end of 1765, when the trustees of Craig's estate required re-payment, Watt owed £757 in capital and accrued interest. The financial position is important in understanding several key developments relating to the history and development of the steam engine. By his own account it was not until 1761 or 1762 that Watt 'tried some experiments on the force of steam in a Papin's Digester', but pressure of business required him to leave these aside. Not until the winter of 1763–1764 did he return to the topic, after being asked to repair the model Newcomen engine belonging to the natural philosophy class of the University. Given this timetable, Craig's money was certainly not being invested directly or indirectly in steam-engine development. Nor could the potential of the separate condenser (Watt dates the idea to the spring of 1765) explain the loan of £150 made by Black to the partnership in June 1763.[38] Presumably Black, like Craig, saw the young man's business as an investment, a loan to him as safe and paying as good a return as would other investments.[39]

Craig's death in April 1765 and the need to pay the executors might have put Watt in severe financial difficulties, but the debt was paid and the instrument business carried on as before. The new investor was the industrial entrepreneur and manufacturing chemist John Roebuck, then involved in the development of a new iron works at Carron. Roebuck had attended Black's chemistry lectures in Glasgow and they had become friends. In the summer of 1765 Black introduced Watt, then busy with ideas about steam engines, to Roebuck, at whose works were a number of Newcomen engines. Watt reported the progress of his experiments on model engines to Roebuck, sold him a microscope and a guitar for Mrs Roebuck, visited Carron, and agreed to try out larger-scale experiments in engine development there.[40]

On 2 January 1766, at the foot of the ledger page recording his debts to Craig, Watt recorded their transfer to Roebuck.[41] Even before 1765 was out, he had erected a small Newcomen engine at Carron. In addition to the clandestine experimental work at Roebuck's residence, Kinneil House, he erected other Newcomen engines in partnership with Robert Mackell — a 24-inch diameter cylinder (1766) and a 45-inch one (1767). On his own account Watt built a couple of short-stroke engines at Torreyburn and another for Roebuck at Carron. Some of the costs of this work were logged in the workshop cash book; whilst John Gardner, by now the senior journeyman, assisted Watt in the development work undertaken for Roebuck.[42]

Roebuck was impressed by the initial progress that Watt was making, funding further research and the taking out of a patent. The circle of those who knew of Watt's steam-engine developments grew, as did the conviction that he would shortly be able to make a radically more efficient engine. Impressed by what he had seen of the works at Soho, Watt had confided enough to its proprietor Matthew Boulton for Boulton to want to buy into the partnership with Roebuck. The story that follows is well documented and well known. In the context of this paper, attention is drawn to part of Watt's October 1768 letter to Boulton, written immediately after his Soho visit, where Boulton had intimated a wish to take a financial interest:

> By several unsuccessful projects & expensive experiments I had involved myself in a considerable debt before I had brought the theory of the fire engine to its present state. About three years ago a Gentleman who was concerned with me dyed. As I had at that time conceived a very clear Idea of my present improvements & had even made some tryal of them, tho' not satisfactory as has been done since, Doctor Roebuck agreed to take my debt upon him & to lay out whatever more money was necessary either for experiments or securing the Inventions, for which cause I made over to him two thirds of the property of the Inventions; the debt and expenses are now about £1,200.[43]

This is somewhat disingenuous. As I have argued above, the debt to Craig was a loan to the business and, at best, only the later tranches may in part be set against the steam-engine project. Furthermore, Watt is as silent to Boulton as he was to Roebuck about the fact that he himself had monies invested elsewhere.

The literary archives of Watt's instrument-making business are supplemented by a class of evidence that has the potential to shed considerable light on the nature of the manufacturing process. This is the somewhat intractable material evidence, long preserved in the attic workshop of Watt's retirement home at Heathfield, near Birmingham. The total contents of this shrine to the last years of the great engineer were moved lock, stock and barrel to the Science Museum in 1924, and the room reconstructed.[44] The Watt workshop contains various strata of material, relating to different periods of its owner's life. From the instrument business in Glasgow there are printing plates for the register plates of barometers, boxes of lenses, glass tubes for thermometers and barometers, a linear dividing engine for laying out thermometer scales, tools for making flutes, parts of incomplete musical instruments, letter and figure punches for marking out wooden instruments. There are stamps cast to form the signature 'J WATT/GLASGOW', and another made up from individual letters to form 'T LOT'. That this is the name of a well-known Parisian flute maker of the mid-eighteenth century casts an interesting ethical reflection on Watt's marketing activities.[45] A set of half-finished Naperian rods and a pattern for making sectors may date from Watt's own apprenticeship rather than reflect the manufacturing technique of his own workshop. His techniques are well revealed by a whole series of partially completed versions of the perspective drawing apparatus developed in association with James Lind in the 1760s.[46] This material shows quite clearly that where items were being constructed in significant numbers, the workshop manufactured by batch methods, so achieving economies of manufacture and better quality control.

James Watt: surveyor and civil engineer

James Watt's first *Waste Book* reveals how speedily his skills were called upon by his contemporaries. Late in 1758 the typefounder Alexander Wilson together with Joseph Black established a partnership with Watt, 'we stand each one third concerned in profit or loss', to undertake experimental work on clocks. Watt's contribution was seventy-one days' work, paid for by the co-partners at 2s 4d a day.[47] Wilson had turned to Watt for technical assistance of a different nature earlier that year, when the Glasgow Magistrates had commissioned him to work on a survey of the Clyde relating to proposals to improve navigation. Wilson received expenses and a gratuity of £20; Watt's records show £3 15s passed on to him by Wilson 'for attendance at the levelling of the river'.[48] The passing of the Clyde Navigation Act in 1759 provided a context for the publication of the survey of the estuary made by John Watt Snr two decades earlier, and which James Watt had had engraved in Edinburgh by Thomas Phinn and sold on behalf of his brother John.[49]

The assistance given to Wilson was essentially small scale. There was greater responsibility in the work undertaken in 1766 for James Stirling at the metal mines at Leadhills.[50] In 1767, however, Watt became involved in his first major surveying job. With the engineer Robert Mackell he was commissioned by the Glasgow tobacco merchants to survey a route for a canal connecting the east and west coasts of Scotland, joining the estuaries of the Forth and the Clyde. This was not to be a *de novo* survey, rather a studied reaction to John Smeaton's proposals, made at the request of the Board of Trustees for the Encouragement of Fisheries, Manufactures and Improvements in Scotland, and published in 1764. To the consternation of Glaswegians, Smeaton's route bypassed the city. The tobacco merchants wanted a route which terminated in the town. Mackell and Watt duly obliged, their report adding fuel to the ensuing debate about the exact line which the proposed canal should take.[51] This commission led to Watt receiving further work of a similar nature. The following year there was a survey of the River Forth above Stirling to indicate the navigational improvements required.[52] In 1769 the Glasgow Magistrates gave him a joint commission with the city surveyor, James Barrie, to resurvey the Clyde, apparently wanting trusted local men to cross-check the detailed proposals of the English engineer, John Golborne.[53]

In September, a long letter to his confidant in England, William Small, described the progress of work on the experimental steam engine at Kinneil House, referred *en passant* to this commission, explaining:

> I would not have meddled with it had I been certain of being able to bring the engine to bear; but I cannot, on an uncertainty, refuse every piece of business that offers. I have refused some common fire-engines, because they must have taken my attention so up as to hinder my going on with my own. However, if I cannot make it answer soon, I shall certainly undertake the next that offers.[54]

Watt had a continuing commitment to making practicable the steam-engine design outlined in the patent granted in January 1769, but he was well aware that whilst research and development had the potential to yield dividends tomorrow, they did not generate income today. He wrote to Small late in 1769, and again early the next year, explaining delays in alterations to the Kinneil engine, intimating:

> somehow or other [I] got into the good graces of the present magistracy, who have employed me in engineering for them, (as Mr Smeaton terms it;) . . . a canal to bring coals in to the town . . . . Vanity also bade me tell Glasgow people they might be served as well at home as by strangers.[55]

Whilst the merits of Watt's two different proposals for the Monkland Canal were debated in Glasgow, he had other similar projects on which to report. From early May 1770, he was in the field for forty-three days, surveying the route of a proposed canal from Perth to Cupar (Angus) for the Commissioners of Forfeited Estates — Smeaton, their first choice of engineer had declined and suggested either his countryman James Brindley, or Robert Mackell, both of whom turned down the job. Not so James Watt.[56] Smiles notes that he was paid 'only eighty pounds, which included expenses'; Muirhead further comments on the 'equally insignificant recompense' of £30 paid for the further work of preparing the report and the associated map.[57] The implications of inadequate remuneration for their hero are uncalled for. At this date Watt was paying his most valuable journeyman a rate of 9s a week; for the master to earn £80 in six weeks, even if he had to pay one or two field assistants, horse hire and living expenses, still includes a substantial allowance for professional expertise. Watt still had to make his reputation as a civil engineer; he could not expect to command the same level of fees as, for example, the well-established John Smeaton. In 1770 when the Burgh of Hamilton asked the English engineer to quote for a design for a new bridge over the Clyde, he asked for ten pounds. The economically minded magistrates turned to Watt in Glasgow and accepted his quote of seven guineas.[58]

In June 1770 Watt took up his appointment as engineer to the Monkland Canal at an annual salary of £200. The skills required to make a good survey are not the same as those required to bring the plan to fruition, even though the selected route was free from any locks. Supervising construction was a major responsibility, with many new challenges, not the least of which was the management of the host of sub-contractors, with an extensive work force: 'many people here had conceived a much higher idea of my abilities than they merit; they had resolved to encourage a man that lived among them rather than a stranger . . . '[59]. With the benefit of hindsight, the historian can add that the untested Watt was also cheaper. His former colleague Mackell, sub-engineer to the Forth and Clyde Canal Company, had an annual salary of £315, working to Smeaton as head engineer on £500.[60] The Monkland investors, presumably aware of the fees that experienced engineers could command as the canal mania spread from England into Scotland, pitched their fee at a suitable level.

Spending two or three days each week on the Monkland contract still allowed Watt to undertake other activities. In June of 1771 there was a survey for a canal across the isthmus at Tarbet and for a canal to connect Lochs Gilp and Crinan, both undertaken for the Commissioners of Forfeited Estates, following pressure from the Glasgow Magistrates.[61] In 1771 he completed his proposals for improving the harbour at Port Glasgow which were carried out under his supervision in 1773. The 1771 plans for Ayr, in contrast, did not proceed.[62]

By November 1772, over seven miles of the Monkland Canal had been completed, including a supply reservoir, an aqueduct and seven road bridges. Construction costs had more-or-less utilised the share capital. The collapse of Douglas, Heron and Co., the Ayr Bank, on 24 June 1772 had major repercussions on commercial and industrial life across the west of Scotland. Work on the Monkland Canal slowed and had more-or-less ceased by the spring of 1773. Completion of the final two miles proposed by Watt was delayed for nearly a decade.[63]

Watt surveyed coal-canals to serve Paisley and Campbeltown in 1773, and that year completed his report on making the upper reaches of the Forth navigable.[64] For the Commissioners of Forfeited Estates he undertook an outline survey for a canal to run from Crieff on the River Earn to Campsie Lynn on the Tay, and detailed work on a link between Loch Linnie and the Moray Firth through Glen More.[65] For the town of Greenock Watt designed a reservoir and water supply line, plus harbour improvements, both being carried out under his supervision within a year.[66]

There is no doubt that by 1773 James Watt had made the grade as a member of the emerging profession of civil engineer. Without leaving the country, he had as much work as he could cope with. As engineer to the Monkland Canal Company he had confided to Small, 'I want little but health and vigour to make money as fast as is fit.'[67] Despite the downturn in the economic situation following the Ayr Bank crash, he found additional surveying and engineering work. He was certainly confident of his continued ability to support himself as a civil engineer, for at some time between January 1771 and September 1773 he gave up the instrument-making business; that relating to scientific rather than musical instrument manufacture apparently being continued by his senior journeyman, John Gardner.[68]

James Watt and the Delftfield Company

Re-investment by the commercially successful Glasgow tobacco merchants played a significant role in the industrialisation of the west of Scotland. Ventures in new industries, such as tanning, iron working, printing and glass were in part a form of diversification. At the same time, such industries produced goods suitable for export to the stores and depots that the tobacco merchants maintained in the colonies.[69] In 1748, Laurence Dinnwiddie, a former provost of Glasgow and a leading tobacco merchant, acquired land with extensive clay deposits. He and three partners established a company to erect the first pottery in the town, with the intention of producing tin-glazed, cream-coloured earthenware (Delftware) in the style of that successfully manufactured in Holland and copied in England by potters in London and Liverpool. English craftsmen were recruited from Lambeth by Laurence Dinnwiddie's elder brother Robert, then trading as a merchant in London. None of the partners had knowledge of any of the various processes involved in making pottery. Initial problems with the kiln caused friction between the partners and their young English manager and his workforce. However, by the early 1750s the Delftfield Company was in successful production, although finding it difficult to compete with the quality and price of pottery being retailed in Glasgow from the well-established English manufacturers.[70]

In May 1764 Laurence Dinnwiddie died. In August and September of 1765, and again in May of 1766, the whole concern was offered for sale. In 1765 another of the original partners transferred his shares to four men, all Freemasons, and in the same lodge as both the brother of another partner and the lawyer dealing with the proposed sale of the business.[71] In June 1763 James Watt himself had joined a Glasgow lodge, and thus had a closer relationship with Freemasonry than is intimated by John Robison's recounting of the commission *c*1761 to make an organ for a 'mason lodge' as the incentive to make and sell musical instruments.[72] The exact nature of Watt's relationship with the Delftfield Company is still unclear. However, following his marriage in July 1764, he moved into the house on the corner of Delftfield Lane that had been built by the Company for their manager.[73] It was on the Company's premises that he began experimenting on the steam engine.[74]

By 1768 the reconstituted Delftfield Company appears to have been back in business, Watt reporting to Joseph Black: 'I now have a small share in the Delft work along with a new company. We intend carrying on a stone manufactory likewise, and are getting people for that purpose.' The handful of letters that then passed between Watt and Black on the topic indicate that, if Watt was only a sleeping partner, he had made himself particularly well informed about the various aspects of the manufacture of pottery.[75] In the following year a letter to Small expresses his exasperation:

> Our pottery is doing tolerably, tho' not as I wish. I am sick of the people I have to do with, tho' not of the business, which I expect will turn out a very good one. I have a fine scheme for doing it all by fire or water mills, but not in this country, nor with the present people.[76]

The nature and form of Watt's activities relating to the Delftfield Pottery remains to be investigated. The extent of his financial interest in midsummer 1772 is recorded in his own journal, and indicates that as businessman and investor he had not sunk all his personal capital, nor loans made to him by others, into the development of the steam engine:

> My Capital in the Delfthouse is now £474 4s 2d besides £20 of interest to be speedily paid me. I owe of this to Mr Moreheid £120 and to Nancy Miller £110, both with one years interest my free capital there being £244 4s 2d.[77]

In the event, Watt retained his financial interests in the Delftfield pottery. As a co-partner living in the English midlands, he cannot have taken a particularly active management role. In his retirement, and having achieved a reputation as the engineer of his age, his views may have carried additional weight with the other partners. Presumably when James Watt Jr purchased land from the Glasgow Delft Company in 1817, the partners as a whole were satisfied that they received the best price.[78]

Envoi

For historians of the steam engine, the story picks up when Matthew Boulton took over from the financially embarrassed John Roebuck to become the business partner of James Watt. During the summer of 1773 the experimental engine at Kinneil was dismantled and the parts sent to Soho. Watt continued to earn money surveying, unable to make the journey south to supervise re-erection and the continuation of the trials. In September, alerted of his wife's illness by a letter from his cousin Robert Muirhead, he left off surveying along the line where Thomas Telford would later build the Caledonian Canal, and raced back to Glasgow. By the time he arrived, he had been a widower for four days. Winter work surveying the upper reaches of the Forth only increased his depression. The astute Boulton chose the right psychological moment to press the invitation to come to Soho. Here was an opportunity for a clean break away from memories and a general worry about indebtedness. On offer to Watt was financial security and an environment that provided the resources to work on a problem whose technical solution had always seemed just in reach.

In the spring of 1774 James Watt left Glasgow and settled in the English midlands. By the end of the year he could report to his father:

> The business I am here about has turned out rather successful, that is to say, that the fire engine I have invented is now going, and answers much better than any other that has yet been made; and I expect that the invention will be very beneficial to me.[79]

As historians of the steam engine have demonstrated, the road to that success was not totally straightforward. There is no doubt that the invention was beneficial, with Watt and Boulton being the first to reap a substantial harvest. Yet the technical significance and commercial impact of Soho on steam-engine development should not be allowed to overshadow the variety of Watt's interests and activities during his Glasgow years. No matter how great the impact of the activity stimulated by the commission to repair the model Newcomen engine, account must be taken of Watt's work as manager of an instrument-making business, as a retailer of 'toys' and toiletries, as surveyor and civil engineer, and as an investor and technical advisor to the Delftfield pottery. The whole spread of activities needs to be seen and judged for their role in the context of the burgeoning of urbanisation and industrialisation in eighteenth-century Scotland. To be sure, Scotland could provide neither the infrastructure in mechanical engineering, nor the capital, nor the markets and marketing skills that Boulton could conjure up for the Watt engine. Yet the myth of Watt as a frustrated pioneer of steam, scratching a living in Scotland until able to make good in England, obscures too rich a slice of Scottish history to be relegated to the preliminaries of the traditional paean to steam. The activities of James Watt 'of Glasgow, in Scotland, Merchant'[80] are in themselves worthy of study.

Notes and references

1 Carnegie, A, *James Watt,* Famous Scots Series (Edinburgh and London: Oliphant & Co., 1905), pp13–14. The source of the story is *Memorandum of the Early Years of Mr Watt,* by his cousin Mrs Marion Campbell (born Muirheid, daughter of his mother's brother) who was his companion in early youth, and friend through life; dictated to and written down by her daughter Miss Jane Campbell in 1798. The *Memorandum* was used by Arago for the biographical memoir on Watt read to the French Academy of Sciences — Arago, D F J, *Eloge Historique de James Watt* (Paris: 1834) — where the anecdote is retold. Arago's account was first available in English as 'Biographical memoir of James Watt', *Edinburgh New Philosophical Journal,* 27 (1839), pp221–97, see p225; reprinted as a distinct publication: Arago, D F J, *Life of James Watt* (Edinburgh: 1839). The memorandum itself is printed in part in Muirhead, J P, *The Life of James Watt* (London: 1854), p20, where Arago's comment is translated (p21) as: 'the little James before the tea-kettle becomes the mighty engineer preluding to the discoveries which were to immortalise him'; see also Arago, [D F J], *Historical Eloge of James Watt,* translated with additional notes by James Patrick Muirhead (London: 1839). Later in life, in a 'Notebook of experiments on heat' dating from about 1764/1766 Watt himself describes and illustrates an experiment whereby he 'took a bent glass tube & inverted it into the nose of a tea kettle . . .' — see Robinson, E and Musson, A E, *James Watt and the Steam Revolution* (London: Adams and Dart, 1969), pp39–40.

2 Smiles, S, *Self-Help, with Illustrations of Conduct and Perseverance* (London: 1859); in print throughout the nineteenth and well into the twentieth century, with additions being added to the text up to the 1866 printing.

3 I was awakened to this factor through reading Emmerson, G S, *John Scott Russell: a Great Victorian Engineer and Naval Architect* (London: John Murray, 1977) and Emmerson, G S, 'L T C Rolt and the *Great Eastern* affair of Brunel versus Scott Russell', *Technology and Culture,* 21 (1980), pp553–69; Buchanan, R A, 'The *Great Eastern* controversy; a comment', *Technology and Culture,* 24 (1983), pp98–106; and Emmerson, G S, 'The *Great Eastern* controversy: in response to Dr Buchanan', *Technology and Culture,* 24 (1983), pp107–13. Buchanan, R A, *The Engineers: a History of the Engineering Profession in Britain 1750–1914* (London: J Kingsley, 1989), pp16–27 provides a valuable summary and commentary on biographical studies of British engineers.

4 Muirhead, J P, *The Origins and Progress of the Mechanical Inventions of James Watt, Illustrated by His Correspondence* (London: 1854), I, ppi–xiii

5 Muirhead, J P, *The Life of James Watt,* pp32–34; family papers indicate one year for the Glasgow apprenticeship; the two, three or four years given in various nineteenth-century accounts can be discounted.

6 Daumas, M, *Les Instruments scientifiques aux XVII et XVIII siècles* (Paris: Presses Univeritaires de France, 1953), p299 *et seq.*; Turner, G L'E, 'A very scientific century', in Forbes, R J *et al.* (eds), *Martinus van Marum: Life and Work* (Leiden: H D Tjeenk Willink for Hollandsche Maatschappij der Wetenschappen, 1973), 4, pp3–38; Turner, G L'E, 'The London trade in scientific instrument making in the 18th century', *Vistas in Astronomy,* 20 (1976), pp173–82

7 *British Public Characters* [1802–1803], (London: 1803), 5, p503. This account is mined for the obituary in *Gentleman's Magazine*, 89 (1819), pp275–76, and the memoir by W Playfair in *Monthly Magazine or British Register*, 48 (1819), pp230–39; the compiler of the biography of Watt in *Penny Cyclopaedia*, 27 (1843), pp135–43 has the honesty to cite the original source.

8 Stuart, R, *A Descriptive History of the Steam Engine* (London: 1824), p98

9 Muirhead, J P, *The Life of James Watt*, p36, citing letter, Watt to J Watt Snr, 2 Sept 1755 — 'If it had not been for Mr Short, I could not have found a man in London that would have undertaken to teach me, as I now find that there are not above five or six that could have taught me all I wanted.'

10 Stuart, R, *Historical and Descriptive Anecdotes of Steam Engines* (London: 1829), I, pp219–20

11 Smiles, S, *Lives of Boulton and Watt* (London: 1865), p100

12 Coutts, J, *History of the University of Glasgow* (Glasgow: J Maclehose, 1909), p288; Lloyd, J T, 'Item Ane shipe Skine: an account of early experimentation in the Natural Philosophy Department', *College Courant, Journal Glasgow University Graduates Association*, 21 (1969), pp5–9

13 Lumsden, H and Aitkin, P H, *History of the Hammermen of Glasgow* (Paisley: Alexander Gardner, 1912), p294; Anderson, J R (ed), *Burgess and Guild Brothers of Glasgow 1573–1750* (Edinburgh: Scottish Record Society, 1925), p424; Renwick, R (ed), *Extracts from the Burgh Records of Glasgow 1739–1759* (Glasgow: Corporation of Glasgow, 1911), pp327, 522, 530; Renwick, R, *Extracts from the Burgh Records of Glasgow 1760–1780* (Glasgow: Corporation of Glasgow, 1912), p3

14 Bryden, D J, 'The Jamaican observatories of Colin Campbell FRS and Alexander MacFarlane FRS', *Notes and Records of the Royal Society of London*, 24 (1970), pp265–68

15 Watt, J, *Waste Book 1757–63*, City of Birmingham Reference Library, Muirhead Collection; the move to Glasgow is recorded on 2 August 1757.

16 Coutts, J, pp258–63

17 Cleland, J, *The Rise and Progress of the City of Glasgow* (Glasgow: 1820), pp97–98. An abridged version of Cleland's account was reproduced in Farey, J, *A Treatise on the Steam Engine* (London: 1827), I, pp309–10. Coutts, J, pp258–63, sketches the relationship of the Foulis Brothers with the University; Cleland was in error in suggesting that the printing works was in the College buildings — it was the Academy of Fine Arts which was allowed rooms.

18 Bryden, D J, *Scottish Scientific Instrument-Makers 1600–1900* (Edinburgh: Royal Scottish Museum, 1972), pp3–4; Bryden, D J, 'Scotland's earliest calculating device; Robert Davenport's Circles of Proportion of c.1650', *Scottish Historical Review*, 55 (1976), pp54–60

19 *Waste Book 1757–63*, 6.12.1757, 7.10.1759; *Glasgow Journal*, 1.12.1763

20 The complete document is printed in Robinson, E and McKie, D (eds), *Partners in Science: Letters of James Watt and Joseph Black* (London: Constable, 1970), pp253–56; the first part is in Muirhead, J P, *The Life of James Watt*, pp58–59.

21 Smiles, S, p106; Muirhead, J P, *The Life of James Watt*, p42; Stuart, R, p220 — 'a formidable obstacle presented itself in the shape of a corporation. He was not a burgess, and the rights of some of the trades were considered to be infringed by his fabrication of compass legs, repairing fiddles and fishing rods'; *The Repertory of Patent Inventions*, n.s. 6 (1828), p325

22 Lumsden, H, *Glasgow Herald*, 26.12.1911, reprinted in Lumsden, H and Aitkin, P H, pp394–404

23 *Glasgow Courant*, 25.11.1754; see also *Glasgow Journal*, 9.8.1770 and 27.5.1773

24 Coutts, J, pp263–64

25 Anderson, J R, *Burgess and Guild Brethren of Glasgow, 1751–1846* (Edinburgh: Scottish Record Society, 1935), p59

26 Letter, Watt to J Watt Snr, 15 October 1758, in Muirhead, J P, *The Origins and Progress of the Mechanical Inventions of James Watt*, I, pxxxiii

27 *Waste Book 1757–63*; Alexander McKenzie for 23½ days May/June 1757 @ 15d per day, whilst based in Greenock; James McBrair 35 days Oct/Nov 1757 @ 10d per day; William Downe 10 days Feb 1758 @ 12d per day; Dougal McMillan began a three month contract @ 14s per week from May 1758 and continued to work for Watt (but not full time) until May 1759. Daniel McMillan, who began work @ 3s per week in September 1758,

continued in employment until July 1764.

28 *Waste Book 1757–63, 1765–69, Journeymen Books 1760–64, 1764–71, Ledger 1759–64, 1764–69,* held in City of Birmingham Reference Library, Muirhead Collection

29 Muirhead, J P, *The Origins and Progress of the Mechanical Inventions of James Watt,* I, ppcviii–cx; Smiles, S, pp110–11; Dickinson, H W, *James Watt Craftsman and Engineer* (Cambridge: Cambridge University Press, 1935), pp28–29

30 Robert Allan was employed part time at 7s a week between October 1760 and February 1763; he made violins, bows and guitars. John McLean, a journeyman turner, was indentured for three years from May 1761 at 4s 6d a week, rising to 6s by the third year; he made flutes — his indenture was discharged in July 1766. Hugh MacIntosh worked at 3s 6d a week between July 1763 and June 1764; he made flutes. So too did John Wright working from December 1762 to June 1763 and George Taylor from October 1760 to April 1764, both at 5s a week. *Journeymen Book, passim.*

31 *Waste Book, passim.* For the offer from Claggett see Robinson, E, *An Exhibition to Commemorate the Bicentary of the Lunar Society* (Birmingham: Birmingham Museum and Art Gallery, 1966), p54.

32 *Waste Book, passim.*

33 These percentages are based on an analysis of the *Ledger 1764–69* which records credit sales to fifty-five customers over this period. These sales may or may not be consistent with the cash sales, for which equivalent records are not presently available.

34 Dickinson, H W and Jenkins, R, *James Watt and the Steam Engine* (Oxford: Clarendon Press, 1927), p18; citing an inventory of October 1759.

35 *Waste Book,* 24.10.1757, 19.6.1758, 30.9.1758

36 *Ledger 1759–64,* f14 lists the 'cash borrowed on interest' from May 1760 to final settlement in January 1766. Before turning to John Craig, Watt had earlier borrowed £70 from George Anderson — making a full repayment with interest within seven months; *Waste Book,* 15.6.1759, 25.1.1760. Immediately following the entry noting the repayment, Watt logged borrowings from John Muirheid of £53 (6.10.1759) and £17.3s (25.1.1760) — in essence transferring the loan capital. I identify the lender as his maternal uncle, and find no evidence for the discharge of the loan — but see note 77.

37 *Ledger 1759–64,* f14 — £49 on 3.3.1764.

38 *Ledger 1759–64,* f5; Robinson, E and McKie, D (eds), pp28, 40, 107–10, record the subsequent history of this loan and compounded interest. The bulk of the debt was discharged in 1776, and a final discharge of just over £40 made in 1781. Smiles, S, p150 and Muirhead, J P, *The Origins and Progress of the Mechanical Inventions of James Watt,* I, pciv, claim that Joseph Black had loaned money to Watt to help him pay for the 1769 patent, a claim repeated in Donavon, A L, *Philosophical Chemistry in the Scottish Enlightenment* (Edinburgh: Edinburgh University Press, 1975), p264. Dickinson, H W, *James Watt Craftsman and Engineer,* p46, and Dickinson, H W and Jenkins, R, pp23, 24, 27, conflate Black's loan with that of Craig. Lord, J, *Capital and Steam Power* (London: King & Son, 1923), p77, repeated by Clow, A and Clow, N L, *The Chemical Revolution; A Contribution to Social Technology* (London: Batchworth Press, 1952), p94, indicates that in 1768 Roebuck repaid Black £1,200 borrowed from Watt.

39 In fact the loan to Watt was a great deal safer. Black's money invested elsewhere was caught up in several insolvencies — see Robinson, E and McKie, D (eds), pp29–30.

40 Muirhead, J P, ppci, 6–7; Smiles, S, pp138–39. On Roebuck's pioneering industrial activities in Scotland, see Jardine, G, 'Account of John Roebuck', *Transactions of the Royal Society of Edinburgh,* 4 pt 1 (1798), pp65–87.

41 *Ledger 1759–64,* f14

42 *Waste Book 1765–69, passim* and 27.9.1768, 10.10.1768, 9.11.1788, 12.1.1769 for payments to Gardner for work at Torryburn; *Ledger 1764–69,* f64, 'Doctor Roebucks new engine' books costs of John Gardner (45 days @ 1s 6d) and Murray Osborne (8 days @ 1s 2d) Oct–Dec 1765. These archival records give credence to James Cleland's brief account of Watt's Glasgow years (Cleland, J, p11) which explicitly cites as his authority: 'Mr John Gardner senior, late a respectable Mathematical Instrument Maker in this City. Mr Gardner became Mr Watt's apprentice in 1760, spent twelve years with him, and acted as his assistant at all his experiments on the Steam Engine,

at Glasgow and Kinneil House.' The business activities of John Gardner (1734–1822) are outlined in Clarke, T N, Morrison-Low, A D and Simpson, A D C, *Brass and Glass: Scientific Instrument Making Workshops in Scotland* (Edinburgh: National Museums of Scotland, 1989), pp164–70.

43 Letter, Watt to Boulton, 20 October 1768, in Muirhead, J P, *The Origins and Progress of the Mechanical Inventions of James Watt,* I, pp30–32
44 Dickinson, H W, *The Garret Workshop of James Watt* (London: HMSO for Science Museum, 1927)
45 I am indebted to Mr M T Wright of the Science Museum for identifying T Lot.
46 Muirhead, J P, *The Life of James Watt,* pp50–56
47 *Waste Book 1757–63,* 26.10.1758, 17.11.1758, 18.5.1759; see also Wilson, P, 'Biographical account of Alexander Wilson AM, Professor of Practical Astronomy in the University of Glasgow', *Transactions of the Royal Society of Edinburgh,* 10 (1826), pp287–88
48 *Extracts from the Burgh Records of Glasgow 1739–59* (Glasgow: 1911), p521; *Waste Book 1757–63,* 13.5.1758
49 Williamson, G, *Memorials: the Lineage, Early Life, Education and Development of the Genius of James Watt* ([Greenock]: 1856), pp53–56; see also *Waste Book 1757–63,* 13.5.1758, 21.9.1759, 4.11.1759, 16.6.1760, [ ].2.1761, 27.12.1761; Moir, D G (ed), *The Early Maps of Scotland,* 3rd edn (Edinburgh: Royal Scottish Geographical Society, 1983), 2, p16. For the broader context see Riddell, J F, *Clyde Navigation* (Edinburgh: John Donald, 1979), pp18–30.
50 *Ledger 1764–69,* f59; four days were spent at Leadhills in April 1766, and a further day drawing up the plans.
51 *An Account of the Navigable Canal Proposed to be Cut from the River Clyde to the River Carron, as Surveyed by Robert Mackell and James Watt* (London: 1767); Lindsay, J, *The Canals of Scotland* (Newton Abbot: David & Charles, 1968), p15 *et seq.*
52 Lindsay, J, *The Canals of Scotland,* p189
53 Riddell, J F, pp35–36
54 Letter, Watt to Small, 20 September 1769, in Muirhead, J P, *The Origins and Progress of the Mechanical Inventions of James Watt,* I, p71
55 Letter, Watt to Small, 12 December 1769, 3 January 1770, in Muirhead, J P, *The Origins and Progress of the Mechanical Inventions of James Watt,* I, pp83–85; see also Watt, J, *A Scheme for Making a Navigable Canal from the City of Glasgow to the Monkland Collieries* [Glasgow: 1769]
56 Muirhead, J P, *The Origins and Progress of the Mechanical Inventions of James Watt,* I, pp95, 102–3; II, pp1–2; Lindsay, J, *The Canals of Scotland,* pp185–86; Lythe, S G E, 'James Watt and the Strathmore Canal project', *Transport History,* 1 (1968), pp67–70
57 Smiles, S, p155; Muirhead, J P, *The Origins and Progress of the Mechanical Inventions of James Watt,* I, pcxxix. For the record, Watt billed the Commissioners for £211 4s 4d less £15 received on account. They queried the amount, and after appraisal by Commissioner George Clark, only a further £100 was paid, and that not until May 1772 — see Lythe, S G E, p70.
58 Smiles, S, p156
59 Letter, Watt to Small, 9 September 1770, in *The Origins and Progress of the Mechanical Inventions of James Watt,* II, p2
60 Lindsay, J, 'Robert Mackell and the Forth & Clyde Canal', *Transport History,* 1 (1968), pp285–92; Lindsay, J, *Canals of Scotland,* p20
61 Lindsay, J, *The Canals of Scotland,* p113; see also Robinson, E and McKie, D (eds), pp34–36
62 Watt, J, *Report Concerning the Harbour of Port Glasgow, Made to the Magistrates of Glasgow,* (1771); see also Muirhead, J P, *The Origins and Progress of the Mechanical Inventions of James Watt,* pp83–84; Muirhead, J P, *The Life of James Watt,* p208; Smiles, S, pp156–57; Robinson, E and McKie, D (eds), p30
63 Thomson, G, 'James Watt and the Monkland Canal', *Scottish Historical Review,* 29 (1950), pp121–33; Lindsay, J, *The Canals of Scotland,* pp52–57
64 Watt, J, *A Report Concerning the Navigation of the Upper Part of the River Forth and Communicating it with the Tideway,* in Golborne, J, *Reports to the Lords Commissioners of Police Relative to the Navigation of the Rivers Forth, Gudie and Devon* (Glasgow: 1773); Lindsay, J, *The Canals of Scotland,* pp182, 184
65 Lindsay, J, *The Canals of Scotland,* pp142, 187
66 Williamson, G, pp173–78
67 Letter, Watt to Small, 9 September 1770, in Muirhead, J P, *The Origins and Progress of the Mechanical Inventions of James Watt,* II, p4

68 The last payment recorded in the surviving *Journeymen Books* is dated December 1770. Gardner was certainly in business by September 1773 when he advertised in *Glasgow Journal* 9.9.1773 — see also Bryden, D J, 'John Gardner's coin scale: a Scottish gold coin scale of 1773', *Equilibrium*, no. 1 (1990), pp1301–11. Gardner continued some of Watt's business activities, such as the sale of the solution of silver which Watt had introduced as a marking-ink in the bleaching industry — see Bryden, D J, *Scottish Scientific Instrument-Makers 1600–1900*, p33.

69 Devine, T M, *The Tobacco Lords; a Study of the Tobacco Merchants of Glasgow and Their Trading Activities* (Edinburgh: John Donald, 1975), pp34–51

70 Kinghorn, J and Quail, G, *Delftfield: a Glasgow Pottery 1748–1823* (Glasgow: Glasgow Museums and Art Galleries, 1986), pp7–19

71 Muirhead, J P, *The Life of James Watt*, pp46–47

72 Dickinson, H W and Jenkins, R, p19; it was the Free and Accepted Masons — the Delftfield partners were members of the Killwinning Lodge.

73 Dickinson, H W and Jenkins, R, p21; Kinghorn, J and Quail, G, pp15, 22

74 Cleland, J, p10, citing Watt's senior journeyman John Gardner, '. . . having procured an apartment in the Delft work . . . he shut himself up along with a single assistant and commenced his experiments on the Steam Engine'.

75 Robinson, E and McKie, D (eds), pp8–12; Quail, G, 'James Watt at Delftfield', *Scottish Pottery Historical Review*, no. 6 (1981), pp47–51. Note that on the final leaves of *Waste Book 1765–69*, Watt has scribbled various memoranda — including weights of 'best pickt cobalt' sent to the Delfthouse. Quail, G, p51, notes that Wedgewood, whilst describing Watt as 'ingenious inventor of the late improvements in the steam engine', also adds that he was 'for some years a potter in Scotland'.

76 Letter, Watt to Small, 28 January 1769, quoted in Dickinson, H W and Jenkins, R, p30

77 City Of Birmingham Reference Library, Muirhead Collection; James Watt, *Journal Book*, 14.6.1772. I identify Mr Moreheid as his cousin Robert, son of John Muirhead (d1769) his mother's brother. (Perhaps this loan rolled up that from John Muirhead made in 1760 — see note 36 above.) I suspect that Miss Nancy Miller is an aunt or sister of his wife.

78 Kelly, H E, 'Documents relating to Delftfield', *Scottish Pottery, 15th Historical Review* (1993), pp43–48

79 Letter, Watt to J Watt Snr, 11 December 1774, in Muirhead, J P, *The Origins and Progress of the Mechanical Inventions of James Watt*, II, p79

80 The quotation is from the preamble to the 1769 patent specification — see Robinson, E and Musson, A E, pp60–61. Watt's trade or profession as is also given as 'Merchant' on his Burgess Ticket — see Anderson, J R, p59.

Jonathan Hornblower (1753–1815) and the steam engine: a historiographic analysis

Hugh Torrens

The significance of Jonathan Hornblower's contributions to the development of the steam engine between 1776 and his death in 1815 are clouded by confusion. Historians face enormous problems in assessing his place in history and, in particular, his rivalry with the better-known Matthew Boulton and James Watt in this field, because of a large number of unusually complex factors. These include:

- a serious bias in the survival of both manuscripts and artefacts.
- the unfortunate habit of the Hornblower family of baptising its many children with Christian names beginning with J, causing problems of individual identification.
- that Watt published his own 'view' of history; a privilege denied to Hornblower.
- that Watt survived to see parts of this history used by one of the first professional historians of the steam engine, John Farey Jr (1791–1851).
- previous historiographic practice which sought to balance every person 'pedestalised' with others who were 'demoted'.
- such former 'heroic histories' being repeated by later historians who relied on such secondary sources without checking them. These simply, but wrongly, supported earlier claims that Jonathan Hornblower's case was 'tried' in a court of law and thus that his 'piracy' was 'proven'.

This paper tries to demonstrate fact from fiction in past writings on steam-engine history.

Introduction

The historiography of the steam engine remains to be written and will be complex. The steam engine has proved a powerful symbol, and proponents of its history have often taken strong positions. In this respect, the steam engine has occupied a position rather as the dinosaur does today — a powerful symbol for modern times but equally extinct.

James Watt (1736–1819) is undeniably the most significant improver of the steam engine. His many improvements are well known, and have been described recently by Richard Hills.[1] Watt's place in history is secure and has been assigned thus: 'if one man in the history of the world is to be taken as the author of modern civilisation, it is this melancholy mechanic'.[2] A Scottish university is named after him, as are the unit of power (in English) and the driver of electric trains or trams (in French).

On the other hand, one of Watt's most significant rivals, Jonathan Hornblower (1753–1815), still languishes in obscurity as a historical figure. He came from a Baptist family with a long tradition of steam-engineering skills in Cornwall, where such skills were a vital part of mining. His 'Boulton' (who similarly supported him with funds and engineering facilities) was the ironmaster of Bristol, John Winwood (1732–1810) from Shropshire.[3] Winwood, as Matthew Boulton did for Watt, provided financial backing to develop the compound steam engine which Hornblower had invented. This engine should best be called the Hornblower and Winwood engine. In this, after steam had been made to act first in a smaller cylinder, it was allowed to act again expansively in a larger cylinder compounded to the same beam. This had been conceived by 1776 when Hornblower made a first model, and his invention was granted patent protection in 1781 for the usual term of fourteen years. Hornblower is unquestionably the originator of compound working of steam engines[4] and was equally a pioneer in the expansive use of steam; quite independently, it seems, of Watt.[5]

The historical record of the protagonists

There is an abundant iconography for James Watt, with many extant portraits (e.g. Plate 1) and statues, of which Francis Chantrey (1781–1841) made at least five, including that at Handsworth which Chantrey considered his finest work. In addition Chantrey made at least two busts, and many other statues, medallions and busts by other artists are recorded by R Gunnis.[6] No portrait or other representation of Jonathan Hornblower is known (that several times reproduced is of his brother Jabez Carter Hornblower)[7].

R S Meikleham (1786–1871), one of the first historians of the steam engine, could already in 1824 — within a decade of Hornblower's death —

write 'it must always be a subject of regret that this ingenious man [misnamed as John Hornblower — the one Christian name beginning with J which the Hornblowers had failed to use] should have wasted the best part of his life, *and ruined his fortune* [my emphasis], in a series of selfish attempts to copy Mr Watt's inventions without coming within the letter of the patent [Watt's of 1769]'.[8] But Hornblower is on record as having left 'a considerable fortune'[9] and his surviving will confirms that he 'died quite well off' and left a considerable estate, recorded as 'below £10,000'.[10] These discrepancies show that this historian of the steam engine had been misled and that he too had confused Jonathan Hornblower with his elder brother Jabez Carter Hornblower (1744–1814), whose fortune was indeed 'ruined'.[11]

To discern the status of any two British people, the most accessible sources to check first are surely *The British Museum Catalogue of Printed Books*[12] and the *Dictionary of National Biography*.[13] When we check these to discover the relative merits of Messrs Watt and Hornblower's contributions to steam engineering, we find the record is heavily biased towards the former, as expected. For Watt, *The British Museum Catalogue of Printed Books* up to 1955 lists three columns of entries and three other entries for James Watt and Co., the company he founded to market his copying press. For Jonathan Hornblower Jr, there is no separate entry, merely a notice of the Hornblower family published in 1883 in America, the country to which one of the Hornblower family was the first steam engineer to emigrate.

The *Dictionary of National Bibliography* entry for Watt published in 1899 comprises twelve pages. It was written by the highly respected engineer (and advocate of the internal combustion engine, which was so soon to usurp the steam engine), Sir Frederick Bramwell (1818–1903), who himself appears in a later volume of the *Dictionary*. The entry for Jonathan Hornblower published in 1891 is, on the other hand, less than a single column; forming part of the entry for Jonathan's father, Jonathan Hornblower Snr (1717–1780). It contains six major factual errors. It was written by an obscure writer called Robert Edward Anderson, but at least it is there; the preface to the new 1993 *Missing Persons* volume of the *Dictionary*[14] notes how many new entries this now contains for engineers and other 'practical men', who had escaped the net of earlier volumes.

If we are to get to the bottom of what was clearly, even by the 1890s, an impossibly complex historiographic problem, we must return to some basic principles. First, we must seek out evidence for both sides of the argument. Second, we must pay proportionately greater attention to contemporary evidence and less to that of later date. Finally, we must recall the first duty of the historian: to understand but not to judge.

Confronting the first of these problems, we are in serious difficulties because of the massively unequal survival of records. This is a problem which has frequently bedeviled other historiographic disputes in the history of technology, like that between Humphry Davy and George Stephenson over the safety lamp. The survival of evidence for the 'gentlemanly' Davy with his 'polite' Royal Society connections is enormously greater than that for the rival but 'practical and working-class' Stephenson.[15] In the case of the conflict between Watt and Hornblower, as already noted, Watt's case is available and has been very completely presented in printed works drawing on the surviving personal and business papers of both James Watt and Matthew Boulton. In addition, the papers of their partnership of Boulton & Watt survive as do the letters of John Southern (1758–1815), Watt's assistant and co-partner from 1782 and partner in Boulton, Watt and Co. from 1810, of Thomas Wilson (1748–1820), Boulton and Watt's Cornish agent from 1777 to 1800 and of John Rennie (1761–1821), a former employee of Boulton & Watt.[16] Tony Woolrich points out that it is the survival of both Watt's personal and business papers which has formed such a unique feature of Watt historiography [personal communication].

The papyrophobic nature of engineering

All these papers have survived despite the fact, noted by Samuel Smiles, that many

> engineers, unlike literary men . . . are so much occupied with doing the thing itself, that [they] have not the disposition, even if [they] had the leisure, to write about how it is done . . . [being] self educated; neither caring to put on record what was worthy to be preserved, nor competent to record it.[17]

The problem that Smiles so perceptively addresses is that engineering and technology are, in Derek De Solla Price's word, papyrophobic[18] activities and so we should expect the documentary record of their history to be biased. Historians should have become aware of this problem earlier. The record of the Hornblower side of the argument has survived to a minute degree compared with that for Watt, who was famous and who was 'preserved'.

Whatever the reasons for such a massively[19] one-sided record, their survival misled an earlier generation of steam historians. John Lord could write in 1923 'that the papers of the firm of Boulton and Watt [were] important, . . . as the record of a pioneering engineering firm which for twenty-five years was the *sole* source of steam power in Great Britain'[20] [my emphasis]. Lord claimed that the 321 Boulton & Watt engines then recognised as made by this firm from 1775 to 1800 comprised 100 per cent of those made in Britain over this period. A more recent assessment suggests the true figure for this firm, for that same period, is less than 30 per cent.[21]

More recent British claims for the completeness of the steam-engine record on paper are a little more hesitant. K Baynes and F Pugh claimed in 1981 that 'the appearance of engineering drawings as a fully-fledged medium for communication in the engineering industry coincided neatly, almost too neatly, with the establishment by Matthew Boulton and James Watt of the first factory in the world for the construction of stationary steam engines . . . in 1773'. These same authors then grudgingly admit that 'it may be we are misled by the completeness of the records that have survived from the Boulton and Watt factory — other drawings, now lost, could . . . make them seem more ordinary'.[22] It is difficult to see how lost drawings could do anything of the sort, but the point they make is clear.

Svante Lindqvist in his book *Technology on Trial*, published in 1984, soon reported the survival of drawings dated 1726 for a Newcomen engine house at Dannemora in Sweden. In a fascinating section on these drawings, called 'The uniqueness of the commonplace', he notes his view that drawings of such engines in England would have been by 1760 'far too commonplace for anyone to think them worth preserving in their own right'. Lindqvist here shows a clear awareness of the problems of the historical record, as far as paper is involved.[23]

Evidence from artefacts

Artefacts pose further problems for the historian. The first is the wholly unequal survival of such material for the 'famous' Watt and Boulton faction. A number of more or less 'original' Watt engines survive in the United Kingdom and abroad. Additionally, the complete contents of Watt's workshop with 6000 objects were carefully 'sanctified' and then transferred to the Science Museum collections in 1924.[24] Even Watt's personal geological collection has survived in Guernsey.[25]

A second problem is how such evidence is used by historians when it has survived. The historian often may not understand the evidence afforded by objects, while an engineer may fail in turn to understand the principles of historical analysis. A prime example of the latter, which relates to a Watt survival, is the 'two cylinder Engine, for double action' illustrated by Edward Alfred Cowper (1819–1893), past-president of the Institution of Mechanical Engineers in 1883. This he described as 'an arrangement that has not before been noticed, and of which, it appears, there is no description extant; it is a good example of the ingenuity and inventive genius of James Watt'.[26] In reality it is a model which Boulton and Watt had had made of the Jabez Carter Hornblower and David Maberly engine for use in a court case against them. In this Boulton and Watt successfully, and rightly, were awarded judgement in 1796 that this engine was a piracy.[27]

For the Jonathan Hornblower side, the situation of survivals is completely different. No significant artefacts whatever seem to have survived, certainly none of his engines. From the archives, Rhys Jenkins, writing in 1931, was able to quote from only two letters which had survived in the papyrophilic Boulton and Watt archives.[28] Since then the situation has improved, thanks to the work of A C Todd on the archives of Davies Gilbert (1767–1839), which cover the years 1790–1814,[29] and the present writer,[30] but there is no major Hornblower archive.

Historiography of the steam engine up to James Watt's death (1819)

The printed books on James Watt and the steam engine reveal some remarkable facts. The earliest 'historical' notice of the steam engine, in the bibliography in the standard work on the Watt steam engine,[31] is John Robison's 'Article on the steam engine' published in the Edinburgh-based *Encyclopaedia Britannica* in 1797.[32] Robison was both a fellow Scot and a personal friend of Watt's. But one notices a strange gap in this bibliography between

1799 (when the trials about the validity of the Watt patent of 1769 were settled) and 1818, the date of Watt's own 'revision' of these Robison articles as a private publication.

Robison's description of the Jonathan Hornblower engine, which in large part used material supplied by Hornblower and Davies Gilbert themselves, was positive; first it was illustrated, in a full plate (pl. 480) — a privilege otherwise granted to only the Watt engine (pl. 479). Robison devoted paragraphs 80–84 of his article to the Hornblower engine which he 'excepted' from his previous criticisms of ignorant or dishonest engineers. This exception was earned, Robison said, on account of the 'singularity and the ingenuity and real skill which appears in some particulars of the construction' of the engine. Robison concluded that the Radstock engine built in 1781–1782, which he then illustrated as having a separate conical condenser (L), was 'stopped by Watt's [1769] patent'. But, crucially, he then noted that if condensation was 'performed as in Newcomen's engine or at least in cylinder A' or, as he put it elsewhere, 'if condensation was confined to a small *part of the cylinder* A, Mr Hornblower has erected engines clear of Mr Watt's patent which are considerably superior to Newcomen's: so has Mr Symington.'[33] These are clear indications that, in Robison's opinion, neither of these last constructions constituted an infringement of Watt's patent of 1769 and that the point at issue was whether a separate condenser was used.

The *Encyclopaedia Britannia* account by Robison was reprinted unchanged in the next edition in 1810[34] after Robison's death in 1805. In 1801 a supplement had been issued[35] in which some 'corrections' were published, from information supplied by Watt himself to Robison.[36] It was now claimed that steam engines had been 'early put into practice' by Watt, working expansively 'about the year 1775' and that such an engine had been erected at Soho 'in 1776'. The true dates seem in both cases to be 1777.[37] The only conclusion to be drawn from these 'revised' dates is that Watt wanted to pre-empt the 1776 date when Jonathan Hornblower had started his expansive compound experiments with a model. One other comment in this supplement is also of significance, as we shall see. It reads '[Jonathan] Hornblower was, we believe, working with Boulton and Watt before that time [1782], we think it fully more probable that he has in this respect profited by the instruction of such intelligent employers'.

In 1807 Olinthus Gregory (1774–1841) published a second edition of his famous *Treatise on Mechanics*.[38] (Plate 2) This now included 'an account of the History of the Steam engine' written by Jabez Carter Hornblower. It was according to the *Dictionary of National Bibliography* article on Gregory, separately reprinted in both 1807 and 1809.[39] It was written while Jabez was imprisoned for debt (because of Boulton and Watt's vendetta) in the King's Bench Prison from 'about 1803 to 1805'[40] and so was hardly complimentary about Watt, but it opened with magnanimity:

> We are by no means disposed to detract one atom from the advantages resulting to the community through the perfection of Mr Watt's engine: but we see it made use of for invidious purposes; not to elevate Mr Watt above his inherent merit, but to subordinate every other professional man in the scale of comparison, to repress the energies of his contemporaries, and give a deadly blow to competition.

James Watt Jr was clearly angry when this account appeared, and his father responded in a letter of November 1808 in answer to some of the points made by Jabez. A second supporting statement by James Lawson and William Murdoch in answer to these claims is also preserved in manuscripts at Doldowlod, and both were published in 1969.[41] In the letter dated 12 November 1808 to his son James Jr, Watt wrote,

> as to their coadjutor [Olinthus] Gregory, it may be proper to give him such answers as may lessen his readers credence in his veracity and discrimination, so as if possible to lessen the evil his books may do, and if a number or two of his *Pantologia* [an encyclopaedia Gregory helped publish between 1802 and 1813] were reviewed it might possibly lessen the number of his dupes.

In the event it was Gregory's 1807 *Treatise* and not his *Pantologia* which was chosen for such attack.

The Watt camp succeeded in forcing Gregory to suppress this Account in later editions (third, 1815; fourth, 1826) of his *Treatise*. These both carried a footnote noting the 'calumny and misrepresentation' Gregory had been exposed to for inserting 'the Account'.[42] This suppression has since quite clearly helped the Account to sink into the oblivion which the Watts hoped for it. A vituperative printed correspondence had followed its first publication[43] in which Gregory noted that Watt 'was too much actuated by a spirit of monopoly for a genuine philosopher' and that Watt and his friends had still often left Jabez 'Hornblower's positions untouched'. One of these 'positions' was Jabez's flat denial that his brother, Jonathan, had ever 'worked for Boulton and Watt or profited by their instruction'; but the suppression of Jabez's Account has meant that this early attempt to refute the first major myth about the Hornblower compound engine had failed.

The Edinburgh reviewer who wrote the antagonistic review of Jabez Hornblower's Account was John Playfair (1748–1819).[44] Playfair noted that the Hornblower compound engine had been commended by Robison in 1797 but also that the account had omitted to mention 'that in the year 1799 it became the subject of an action, as an infringement of Mr Watt's patent'.[45] The choice of words was no doubt careful, but historians should not as a result assume, as they so often have since, that becoming the subject of an action-in-law meant that an infringement was proved in law against Hornblower or his compound engine. English law proclaims one innocent until proven guilty. The true situation in this 'action' can be established from a further contemporary document which was also produced in response to Jabez's Account, as we shall see below.

When Robison's *Articles on Steam and Steam Engines* was planned for republication in 1813/1814, Watt was asked to revise it. Its first republication was in 1818 in a limited edition by Watt of only fifty copies.[46] It was finally issued again in 1822 as volume 2 of Robison's *System of Mechanical Philosophy.*[47] In these reprints the new title page notes only that there were 'notes and additions' but there were also some significant subtractions. In particular, paragraphs 80–87 of Robison's original text are omitted (between paragraphs 76 and 77 of Watt's revised versions).[48] Watt noted only that

> Dr Robison's account of Hornblower's engine has been omitted by the Editor, as unsuitable to the present work. Notwithstanding the great ingenuity evinced by Mr Hornblower in the construction of his engine, yet it was found by a court of law to be a plagiarism of Mr Watt's invention, and on this account Mr Watt could not have made any commentary upon it, even if it had appeared deserving of insertion.

If others soon noticed the omissions, they were puzzled by them.[49] Watt also removed those paragraphs which Robison had devoted (paragraphs 85–87) to Watt's own attempts at developing a rotary engine. This omission, which suggests that Watt thought this work was now best forgotten, is another point of considerable historiographic importance.

The real significance of Watt's editorial removals in 1818 is the incorrect claim he inserted about a legal decision having been made against the Jonathan Hornblower engine. Jonathan himself had made it clear that this was untrue, immediately after his brother's quite different engine had been found to be a piracy and the Watt patent had been validated. He arranged for the publication of this notice in one of the most widely circulated newspapers in Cornwall in 1799, 'We are requested to state to our readers that the case lately decided in the Court of the King's Bench "Boulton & Watt against Hornblower" has no reference whatever to Mr Jonathan Hornblower of Penryn in Cornwall . . .'[50]. But the damage was done and the second of the most enduring myths of the rivalry between Watt and Hornblower, namely that the latter's engine was a 'proven piracy', had been created, once again by Watt himself.

The protagonists of anti-Hornblower historiography thus far, Robison and Playfair, were both Scots (as was Watt) and personal friends of Watt. One gets a strong impression from their writings that Scottish eulogies of Watt were being constructed, like the much later biography of Watt which Andrew Carnegie (1835–1919), another famous Scot, produced in 1905 in the *Famous Scots Series.*[51] Such nationalistic pleadings should have no place in history, but the long controversy between the French and the British as to who had invented the steam engine reminds us how powerful such motives can be.[52] This nationalist rivalry again reared its head, after Watt's death, over the contributions made by the French to the Watt engine.[53] John Farey Jr (1791–1851) was one of those involved in showing how French contributions had been misrepresented by partisan Wattite biographers. The first historical treatment of the steam engine by this remarkable man had appeared in October 1816 in A Rees' *Cyclopaedia.*[54] This predated Watt's private revision of 1818 of Robison's *Encyclopaedia Britannia* articles, although often wrongly recorded as having been published in 1819 and thus after Watt's own revision.[55]

Historiography of the steam engine after the death of James Watt

After James Watt's death in 1819, the major

historical treatises are John Farey's of 1827,[56] which expands his 1816 treatment above, and Thomas Tredgold's (1788–1829), also of 1827.[57] The authors were close friends and shared similar attitudes to history. They also differed from most of the previous generations of writers on the history of the steam engine, as both were professional writers and technically expert and well informed; moreover they were both English, not Scottish. Farey's book has been (rightly) described thus: 'there is a strong, perhaps overwhelming, case for seeing Farey's volumes as the finest monographs on technology produced during the Industrial Revolution'.[58] But as history it may not always reach the same high standard because Farey was an employee of Watt's from at least August 1814 and was able, in part, to use Watt's view of history from the several personal visits that Watt made to help the Fareys before the *Cyclopaedia* article was published in 1816.[59] Jonathan Hornblower had died in 1815 and no such personal contacts or view of history were available to Farey. Despite Farey's close friendships with Olinthus Gregory, and others who had taken sides in the Watt–Jonathan Hornblower dispute, like Joseph Bramah (1748–1814), Farey offered no opinion on the merits of the battle between Watt and Hornblower in his discussion of the Hornblower engine in his *Treatise*. It seems clear that he wished to remain neutral on a case which was still so deeply disputed.

Tredgold was more pro-Hornblower in his treatment of the Watt–Hornblower controversy. Tredgold had less personal contact with Watt but his book, unlike Farey's, went to a second edition in 1838.[60] Tredgold had died in 1829 and the second edition was entrusted to Wesley Stoker Barker Woolhouse (1809–1893). He was a mathematician and astronomer but his limited knowledge of steam engines was offset as the new edition was 'enlarged by the contributions of eminent scientific men'. Again no mention was made of sections omitted from the first edition in this edition but, as a writer soon asked, 'can any explanation be afforded of the suppression of Tredgold's views respecting the publication of Watt's expansion'[61] in this new edition? The reason is, however, clear. Tredgold had argued for Hornblower's 'priority' in the suppressed section.

Tredgold's second edition of 1838 was soon followed in 1839 by a translation of D F J Arago's *Eloge of Watt*[62] by James Patrick Muirhead (1813–1898). William Playfair, when he accused the French of plagiarism in 1819,[63] had written tellingly, 'it is to be hoped that as both Mr Boulton and Mr Watt left sons, they will cause this matter [the French theft of Watt's ideas] to be set to rights.' In the event, James Watt Jr (1769–1848), who was highly jealous of his father's reputation, made Muirhead his father's literary executor. Muirhead was a Scottish advocate, not an engineer. He published widely on Watt.[64] He was a cousin of Watt's through both Watt's mother[65] and Watt's first wife and was also connected with Matthew Boulton, because in 1844 he had married one of Boulton's granddaughters.[66] His view of the Watt–Hornblower controversy must also be treated with care, as he again confused Jabez with his brother and wrongly named Jonathan Hornblower as the co-partner with David Maberly in the pirate engine which was found to be a piracy in a court of law.[67] The many later works dealing, if only in part, with the history of the steam engine naturally followed this now well-established claim and were heavily influenced by the inaccurate historiography which had developed over the previous forty years.

But some people were now beginning to ask if justice had been done to all parties. In 1841 the Institution of Civil Engineers appealed for memoirs of the three Cornish engineers Jonathan Hornblower, Richard Trevithick and Arthur Woolf, and of Watt's 'assistant' William Murdoch.[68] None was received but a small start, at restoring Hornblower at least, was made in 1863 when the journalist Cyrus Redding (1785–1870) published his own memoirs.[69] His mother was Jonathan's sister Joanna. It may have been these memoirs which inspired the entry for Jonathan Hornblower in the *Dictionary of National Bibliography* written by R E Anderson and published in 1891.

R E Anderson and the Hornblower entry in the Dictionary of National Bibliography

Robert Edward Anderson (?1840–?fl1903) contributed a total of fifty-nine entries to the *Dictionary of National Bibliography* between 1882 and 1893 for entries beginning with the letters B and H to K only.[70] Anderson was probably born in 1840 at Comrie in Perthshire. He was a graduate of St Andrews University, which, significantly, is in Scotland. He entered the University in 1859 and left in 1863 after a normal four-year arts course.[71] He graduated with an MA in 1874 and he is noted in St Andrews' records as having been 'a tutor in

England and France and engaged in the Education Department, Whitehall as well as an author and journalist'.[72] His books, as listed in *The British Museum Catalogue of Printed Books*, include a translation from French (1877) and books on English history (some for schools, 1884 and 1897) and on anthropology (1896, 1899 and 1903). He also contributed two biographical articles to the ninth edition of the *Encyclopaedia Britannia* in 1883 and 1889. His credentials to write with any authority on engineering biography were clearly non-existent and we may well be justified in using here that well-tried word 'hack' in regard to his contributions in that field.

In view of Anderson's limitations and the misleading historiography, it is not surprising that Anderson, in his short entry for Jonathan Hornblower Jr:

- mistakenly gives him a second Christian name Carter.
- miscredits him with the invention of the double-beat valve.[73]
- wrongly repeats that he had been a former employee of Watt's.
- again confuses Jabez's engine, which was both a piracy and was found to be a piracy in a court of law, with Jonathan's, which Jonathan and many others said was not pirated.
- wrongly states that the law-suit against Jonathan Hornblower over his engine, patented in 1781 and which became the subject of a suit with Boulton and Watt in 1799, was legally decided against Hornblower.
- wrongly credits all the publications of Jabez Carter Hornblower (Jonathan's elder brother) between 1798 and 1805 to Jonathan.
- wrongly credits Jabez Hornblower with writing the article on steam engines in Olinthus Gregory and John Mason Good's encyclopaedia *Pantologia* (1802–1813) when that article was almost certainly by John Farey Jr, who certainly drew the plates for it.[74] Anderson clearly confused this with Jabez's contribution to Gregory's *Treatise* in 1807.

These errors and their sources must be detailed in turn.

- The family tree of the Hornblower's, whose Christian names all began with J, is complex, but it had been clarified by Nelson in 1883.[75] He had clearly shown that only Jabez had the second Christian name Carter so Jabez Carter's publications could have been correctly separated from those few of Jonathan's. The confusion of these two stems from the long obfuscation of the true relationship between Jabez and Jonathan and that their engines were the same.
- The invention of the double-beat valve had already clearly, and correctly, been assigned to Joseph Hornblower (1755–1822), another brother, by Jabez Hornblower in his suppressed history in 1807.[76]
- The same source had also refuted the claim that Jonathan had ever been an employee of Watt's.
- The confusion of Jabez and Jonathan's engines seems to have been made first by Watt himself in 1818, as we have seen.
- Watt had also promoted the view that Jonathan's engine was found to be a piracy in law. Whether Watt was himself misled over these last facts, or wished to mislead, is a moot point but his statements have since misled countless others.

The never-proven piracy

The final proof that no piracy by Jonathan Hornblower was ever demonstrated comes from Ambrose Weston (1745–1810), Matthew Boulton and James Watt's attorney, writing thus, probably to James Watt Jr, on 19 November 1808, again clearly as a result of the publication of Jabez's Account:

> A writ was served on Jonathan Hornblower on 21 October 1799 and he appeared in the usual manner and declared
> a) that he was not guilty and
> b) that the course of action did not accrue within six years. Boulton and Watt prepared a case *but it was not delivered* [my emphasis], nothing further was done by us in this action. I do not find there was any judgement by default or otherwise. I believe the fact was Mr Robinson Boulton went into Cornwall and frightened the users of Hornblower's engines out of about £40,000 with which being content, the action against Jonathan dropped of course.[77]

In the face of such an appalling concatenation of errors and of 'fact', coupled with the prestige of the *Dictionary of National Bibliography*, some or all of these errors have been endlessly repeated, even by a number of respected historians. New myths have also emerged from the chaos: for example, the claim that Hornblower's 1781 patent, which lapsed in 1795, was somehow 'revoked'.[78] A second more recent canard reports that Jonathan Hornblower had claimed in 1788 that Watt's separate condenser 'had not been a new invention'.[79]

A more recent claim, that Hornblower's application for an extension of his patent rights in 1792 was also 'defeated' at its second parliamentary reading, is also in error. It was in fact withdrawn;[80] a subtle but vital difference.

Such historiography has sabotaged the complex question of exactly what Jonathan Hornblower's engine owed to the Watt engine. This now seems incapable of an accurate answer in view of the mountain of surviving evidence for one side (Watt) against a molehill for the other (Hornblower). But the views of Jonathan Hornblower, a highly religious man whose obituarist particularly noted he was, as a Baptist, 'upright and just in all his dealings, he ever presented himself "the best and noblest work of God — an honest man" ',[81] seems worth ending with. In a letter written in 1789 he confirmed that 'the engine for which I obtain'd a patent of late years [1781] is not to be consider'd as an improvement on W[att]'s because I made a model of it 13 years ago [1776], which is before I had ever heard of such a man'.[82]

Conclusions

We need to take more seriously those previous attempts to render better justice to a significant engineer who happened to be on the losing side of history. Historians have a duty to record losers as well as winners. Previous attempts to do justice to Jonathan Hornblower include those by W Pole in 1844,[83] A Mallet in 1910[84] and T R Harris in 1976.[85] Sadly, however, both Pole and Mallet confuse Jabez with Jonathan, while Harris is poorly served by his publishers, as his careful work lacks any detailed footnotes which are vital in the historical minefield of steam-engine history.

We may end by noting two particular points of interest. The first is that Cornish engineers at least thought that Hornblower's compound engine was superior to James Watt's. In 1792, a trial by Richard Trevithick Snr and Davies Gilbert found the former to have an 'advantage in power . . . as 10 to 16.5+'.[86] The famous Wherry Mine near Penzance, amazingly set amid tidal rocks near Penzance, (Plate 3) was an 'adventure which both in ingenuity and success was probably never equalled in any country'.[87] Its 'ingenuity' depended on a Hornblower compound engine, which started work in 1793.[88] It was described at work by Charles Hatchett in May 1796.[89] This mine proved so profitable that Hornblower and Winwood chose it to establish their claim to premiums on fuel savings over and above those achieved with the Watt engine. Meetings of the Stannary Court were set up and on 3 May 1797 it was decided to refer the dispute (Hornblower *vs* Gundry) to a committee of four. This case was decided in June 1798, after Gilbert had prepared calculations on twenty-three engines working in Cornwall, in Hornblower's favour.[90]

Historians have long assumed that this decision was simply one made by 'treacherous' Cornishmen. But we may ask if this superiority was possible because Hornblower was already using higher-pressure steam? It has long been known that the advantages of compounding using 'strong steam' were already known to him by 'about 1793'. But Jonathan himself had noted in 1789 that he was already using steam at 16 pounds per square inch,[91] pressures higher than 'Mr Watts's [which] seldom work with more than 5 pounds' as late as 1803.[92] Historians have assumed that this knowledge was never put to use by Hornblower because of Watt's opposition. Historians have also too long assumed that the only possible savings from the basic Newcomen engine were those due to Watt. History shows that both these assumptions are over-simplified.

The second point is how Hornblower compound engines have been enumerated. The latest lists give a total of at least fifteen.[93] But a document in the Doldowlod archives shows that John Wilkinson's (1728–1808) Llyn-y-Pandy mines near Mold, Flintshire, had also installed two Hornblower compound engines by 1796.[94] These had in the past been simply recorded as 'pirate' Boulton and Watt engines (as I had earlier feared had happened).[95] It is important to record all pre-1800 steam engines, if improved from the basic Newcomen pattern, not simply as Watt engines. But this is exactly what has been done for Irish engines.[96]

The case of Jonathan Hornblower shows how complex the historiography of steam engineering has become. Two intriguing recent studies suggest that other cases involving engineering history have been distorted by additional problems. The first is the deliberate 'processing' of historical data to support a particular outcome. Such processing by Thomas Telford to belittle William Jessop's reputation has been recently revealed by Charles Hadfield.[97] The second is the deliberate suppression and destruction of evidence. A fascinating, if unproven, case for this having happened is that of William Murdoch (1754–1819), another of the engineers for memoirs of whom the Institution of Civil Engineers appealed in 1841, which has been published by John Griffiths. He discovered only fifty-two letters to Murdoch and only twenty from Murdoch in the 'surviving' archives of Boulton and Watt and Co., although he was not able to gain access to all relevant material. His conclusion was that this anomalous 'survival' of material can be 'explicable only by the removal of letters from the archives'. His more sinister explanation for this is that relevant 'records were "cleaned" ' by Watt's relatives after his death in 1819, during a period when what he calls Wattolatry gained ground.[98] It is a fascinating possibility.

But such conspiracy theories can prove dangerous. Griffiths mentions that the *New Monthly Magazine* memoir of Watt by William Playfair[99] 'so displeased [James] Watt Jr that he entered into a lengthy and bitter correspondence on the subject'. Griffiths seems to have assumed that this was because Playfair had not then been sufficiently adulatory of Watt Snr, when another more compelling reason, as we have seen, could be that Watt Jr was 'displeased' because of the numerous errors of fact he found in Playfair's memoir, which the Fareys had pointed out.

Whatever their causes these two cases, with that of Jonathan Hornblower and the others recorded in this volume, demonstrate the vital need for modern and careful reassessments of some of our major engineering figures. Existing views of their work may prove not to have been as objective in their judgements as today's posterity should demand.

Acknowledgements

I am grateful to Lord David Gibson-Watt for allowing me privileged access to his private papers (these have recently been deposited in Birmingham City Library); Charles Hadfield provided vital encouragement when it was most needed and Tony Woolrich has provided this, much data and a careful and critical appraisal of a first draft.

Notes and references

1 Hills, R L, *Power From Steam: a History of the Stationary Steam Engine* (Cambridge: Cambridge University Press, 1989)

2 Hammond, J L and Hammond, B, *The Rise of Modern Industry*, 7th edn (London: Methuen and Co. Ltd, 1947), p130

3 Torrens, H S, 'Winwoods of Bristol: part one', *Bristol Industrial Archaeological Society Journal*, 13 (1980), pp9–17

4 Jenkins, R, 'Jonathan Hornblower and the compound engine', *Transactions of the Newcomen Society*, 11 (1931), pp138–155, plates xvii–xxi

5 Rolt, L T C, *James Watt* (London: Batsford, 1962), p122

6 Gunnis, R, *Dictionary of British Sculptors 1660–1851* (London: Abbey Library, [1968]). The most famous of Chantrey's Watt statues — that larger-than-life one once placed in Westminster Abbey — was mysteriously replaced by a plaster bust late in 1960 (*The Times*, 22 December 1960, p12). It would be interesting to learn the circumstances behind this replacement.

7 [Harris, T R], 'The Hornblower family', *Journal of the Trevithick Society*, 4 (1976), pp7–44

8 [Meikleham, R S, writing as] Stuart, R, *A Descriptive History of the Steam Engine* (London: Knight & Lacey, 1824), p144

9 Redding, C, *Yesterday and Today* (London: Newby, 1863), 1, p136

10 Buckland, J S P, 'The Hornblower family — additional notes', *Newcomen Bulletin*, 129 (1984), pp4–5

11 [Harris, T R], pp7–44

12 *The British Museum Catalogue of Printed Books to 1955*, 263 vols (London: Trustees of the British Museum, 1965–1966)

13 *Dictionary of National Biography*. The entry for Hornblower in vol. 27 was first published in July 1891 and that for Watt in vol. 60 was first published in October 1899.

14 Nicholls, C S (ed), *Dictionary of National Biography — Missing Persons* (Oxford: Oxford University Press, 1993), pvi

15 Griffin, A R, 'Sir Humphry Davy: his life and work', *Industrial Archaeology Review*, 4 (1980), pp202–13

16 Torrens, H S, 'New light on the Hornblower and Winwood Compound Steam Engine',

Journal of the Trevithick Society, 9 (1982), pp21–41, particularly p22

17 [Smiles, S], 'James Watt', *Quarterly Review*, 104 (1858), p411

18 De Solla Price, D, 'Is technology historically independent of science? A study in statistical historiography', *Technology and Culture*, 6 (1965), p561

19 Tann, J, 'The Archives of Boulton & Watt', *Business Archives*, 43 (1977), pp30–33

20 Lord, J, *Capital and Steam Power 1750–1800* (London: King & Son, 1923), p2

21 Kanefsky, J and Robey, J, 'Steam engines in 18th century Britain: a quantitative assessment', *Technology and Culture*, 21 (1980), p185

22 Baynes, K and Pugh, F, *The Art of the Engineer* (Guildford: Lutterworth Press, 1981), p35

23 Lindqvist, S, *Technology on Trial* (Uppsala: Almqvist & Wiksell, 1984)

24 Dickinson, H W, *The Garret Workshop of James Watt* (London: Science Museum, 1976)

25 Howell, A, 'Guernsey Museum and Art Gallery: natural history collections', *Journal of Biological Curation*, 1 (1989), p16

26 Cowper, E A, 'On the inventions of James Watt, and his models preserved at Handsworth and South Kensington', *Proceedings of the Institution of Mechanical Engineers* (November 1883), pp610–11, plate 69

27 Torrens, H S, 'New light on the Hornblower and Winwood Compound Steam Engine', p21

28 Jenkins, R, p147

29 Todd, A C, *Beyond the Blaze: a Biography of Davies Gilbert* (Truro: Bradford Barton, 1967)

30 Torrens, H S, 'Some newly discovered letters from Jonathan Hornblower (1753–1815)', *Transactions of the Newcomen Society*, 54 (1984), pp189–200

31 Dickinson, H W and Jenkins, R, *James Watt and the Steam Engine*, 2nd edn (Ashbourne: Moorland Publishing, 1981), bibliography pp359–372

32 Robison, J, the articles 'Steam' and 'Steam Engine', in Gleig, G (ed), *The Encyclopaedia Britannica,* 3rd edn (Edinburgh: Bell and Macfarquhar, 1797), 17, pp770–72, plate 480. Watt's initial reaction to Robison's article as far as the Hornblower engine is concerned is recorded in a letter from Watt to Robison dated 24 October 1796 and reproduced by Robinson, E and McKie, D, *Partners in Science* (London: Constable, 1970), pp232–35.

33 Watt, J, *The Articles Steam and Steam-Engines Written for the Encyclopaedia Britannica by the Late John Robison . . . With Notes and Additions by James Watt* (Edinburgh: [printed privately for Watt] John Murray, 1818)

34 Millar, J (ed), *The Encyclopaedia Britannica*, 4th edn (Edinburgh: Constable, 1810)

35 [Robison, J], the article 'Steam Engine', in Gleig, G (ed), *Supplement to the Third Edition of the Encyclopaedia Britannica*, (Edinburgh: Bonar, 1801), II, pp522–24

36 Watt, J, 'History of the origin of Mr Watt's improvements on the steam engine', *Edinburgh Philosophical Journal*, 2 (1820), p2

37 Dickinson, H W and Jenkins, R, pp120–26

38 Hornblower, J C, 'An account of the history of the steam engine', in Gregory, O (ed), *A Treatise of Mechanics*, 2nd edn (London: Kearsley, 1807), II, pp358–90, III, plate 30

39 Hornblower, J C, in Nelson, W (ed), *Historical Review of Improvements in the Steam-Engine in the 18th Century* (Washington: Pearson, 1880), with an introductory notice pp3–4; copy in University of Michigan library

40 Anon., 'The Hornblower family: pioneer engineers', *Journal of the Trevithick Society*, 5 (1977), p67. See also Robinson, E and Musson, A E, *James Watt and the Steam Revolution* (London: Adams and Dart, 1969), p110

41 Robinson, E and Musson, A E, *James Watt and the Steam Revolution*, pp 109–11

42 This footnote was reprinted by Galloway, E, *History and Progress of the Steam Engine* (London: Kelly, 1829), pp96–97.

43 [Playfair, J], 'Account of the steam engine', *Edinburgh Review*, 13 (January 1809), pp326–27; then Gregory, O, 'Misrepresentation in the Edinburgh Reviewer's account of Mr Ol. Gregory's "Treatise of Mechanics" ', *Monthly Magazine* (1 August 1809), pp29–32; then [Anon., the Edinburgh Reviewer's reply], 'Appendix — to Olinthus Gregory', *Edinburgh Review*, 15 ([November] 1809), pp245–54; and finally Gregory, O, 'Dr Olinthus Gregory's second answer to the Edinburgh Reviewers', *Literary Panorama*, 7 (1810), pp694–96. A summary of Gregory's 'Historical account' and the first response from Edinburgh was also published in *Retrospect of Philosophical, Mechanical, Chemical and Agricultural Discoveries*, 5 (1809), pp37–49.

44 John Playfair's authorship of the first hostile

review is documented by Houghton, W E (ed), *The Wellesley Index to Victorian Periodicals 1824–1900* (Toronto: University of Toronto Press, 1966), I, p444.

45 Playfair, J, p327

46 Smeaton, W A, 'Some comments on James Watt's published account of his work on steam and steam engines', *Notes and Records of the Royal Society*, 26 (1971), pp35–42

47 Robison, J, *A System of Mechanical Philosophy, with Notes by David Brewster*, 4 vols (Edinburgh: John Murray, 1822). Vol. 2 reprints Watt's volume of 1818 as a second 'edition' of Watt, J, *The Articles Steam and Steam-Engines Written for the Encyclopaedia Britannica by the Late John Robison.*

48 Watt, J, *The Articles Steam and Steam-Engines Written for the Encyclopaedia Britannica by the Late John Robison*, p14

49 Tredgold, T, *The Steam Engine, Comprising an Account of its Invention . . .*, 1st edn (London: J Taylor, 1827), p216

50 *Sherborne and Yeovil Mercury* (18 February 1799), p4

51 Carnegie, A, *James Watt* (Edinburgh: Oliver Anderson & Ferrier, 1905)

52 Reid, H, *Remarks on Certain Statements Regarding the Invention of the Steam Engine in M Arago's Historical Eloge of James Watt* (Glasgow: Stuart & Co., 1840)

53 Farey, J, [Snr], 'On the alleged plagiarisms of Frenchmen', *Philosophical Magazine*, 56 (1820), pp321–23; Farey, J, [Jr], 'Defence of M De Prony from the aspersions contained in memoir of Mr Watt', *Philosophical Magazine*, 55 (1819), pp110–12

54 [Farey, J, Jr], Article 'Steam Engine' in Rees, A (ed), *The Cyclopaedia or Universal Dictionary*, 34 (London: Longman, Hurst, Rees, Orme & Brown, 1816)

55 Dickinson, H W and Jenkins, R, p365

56 [Farey, J, Jr], *A Treatise on the Steam Engine: Historical, Practical, and Descriptive* (London: Longman, Rees, Orme & Brown, 1827)

57 Tredgold, T, *The Steam Engine, Comprising an Account of its Invention . . .*, p216

58 von Tunzelmann, G N, *Steam Power and British Industrialisation to 1860* (Oxford: Clarendon Press, 1978), p2

59 Dickinson, H W, p18; Farey, J, [Snr], 'On the alleged plagiarisms of Frenchmen', p321–23

60 Tredgold, T, *The Steam Engine: its Invention and Progressive Improvement*, 2nd edn, revised and edited by W S B Woolhouse (London: Weale, 1838)

61 'S S', 'Mr Watt and the discovery of working steam expansively', *Mechanics Magazine*, 44 (1846), pp248–49. The suppressions can be seen by comparing paragraphs 27 and 29 of the two editions. Tredgold's comments about the damaging effects of Watt's steam engine monopoly were now also suppressed in paragraph 52.

62 Arago, [D F J], *Historical Eloge of James Watt*, translated with additional notes and an appendix by James Patrick Muirhead (London: Murray, and Edinburgh: Blackwood, 1839)

63 Playfair, W, 'Memoir of James Watt Esq, FRS', *New Monthly Magazine*, 12 (1819), p580

64 Muirhead, J P, *Correspondence of the Late James Watt on his Discovery of the Theory of the Composition of Water* (London: Murray, and Edinburgh: Blackwood, 1846); *The Origin and Progress of the Mechanical Inventions of James Watt*, 3 vols (London: Murray, 1854); *The Life of James Watt* (London: Murray, 1858) and 2nd edn (1859) with an American edition (New York: Appleton, 1859)

65 Dickinson, H W and Jenkins, R, p11

66 Pirie-Gordon, H (ed), *Burke's Genealogical and Heraldic History of the Landed Gentry*, 15th edn (London: Shaw Publishing Co. Ltd, 1937), p1645; Pine, L G (ed), *Burke's Genealogical and Heraldic History of the Landed Gentry*, 17th edn (London: Burke's Peerage Ltd, 1952), p232

67 Muirhead, J P, *The Origin and Progress of the Mechanical Inventions of James Watt* (New York: Appleton, 1859), p305

68 Anon., 'The Council invite communications on the following as well as other subjects for Telford and Walker premiums', *Civil Engineer and Architect's Journal* (December 1841), p433

69 Redding, C, p136

70 Fenwick, G, *Index to the Contributors to the Dictionary of National Biography 1885–1901* (Winchester: St Pauls, 1989), pp4–5

71 Anderson, J M, *The Matriculation Roll of the University of St Andrews* (Edinburgh: Blackwood, 1905), pp127, 131, 133, 138

72 Letter from Smart, R N, Keeper of the Muniments, University of St Andrews, 5 July 1993

73 [Harris, T R], p43

74 Personal communication from Woolrich, A P

75 Nelson, W, *Josiah Hornblower and the First Steam-Engine in America* (Newark, NJ: Daily Advertiser Printing House, 1883)
76 Hornblower, J C, 'An account of the history of the steam engine', p378
77 Letter, Ambrose Weston to James Watt ?Jr, 19 November 1808, Birmingham Public Library, Boulton and Watt archives, Muirhead Box 4 W
78 This was apparently a new hare started by Appleby-Millar, R N, 'Some early Compound Engines AD 1776–1845', *Edgar Allen News*, 20 (1941), pp753–55 and repeated since, see von Tunzelmann, G N, p24
79 Rowe, J, *Cornwall in the Age of the Industrial Revolution* (Liverpool: Liverpool University Press, 1953), p96. Hornblower and Winwood made no such claim in 1788 (see Torrens, H S, 'New light on the Hornblower and Winwood Compound Steam Engine', p29), merely that they had not used the separate condenser. See also Torrens, H S, 'Some newly discovered letters from Jonathan Hornblower (1753–1815)', pp196–200
80 Torrens, H S, 'Some newly discovered letters from Jonathan Hornblower (1753–1815)', p193
81 Anon., '[Obituary of Jonathan Hornblower]', *Monthly Magazine*, 39 (1815), pp286–87
82 Torrens, H S, 'Some newly discovered letters from Jonathan Hornblower (1753–1815)', p191
83 Pole, W, *A Treatise on the Cornish Pumping Engine* (London: Weale, 1844)
84 Mallet, A, 'Evolution practique de la machine á vapeur', *Memoires de la Sociëté des ingénieurs civils de France* (1910), pp6–57
85 [Harris, T R], pp7–44
86 Dickinson, H W and Titley, A, *Richard Trevithick: the Engineer and the Man* (Cambridge: Cambridge University Press, 1934), plate 3
87 Hunt, R, *British Mining* (London: Crosby Lockwood, 1877), pp77–80
88 Barton, D B, *The Cornish Beam Engine* (Truro: Bradford Barton, 1969), p271; Russell, A, 'The Wherry Mine, Penzance', *Mineralogical Magazine*, 28 (1949), p523
89 Raistrick A, *The Hatchett Diary* (Truro: Bradford Barton, 1967), p33
90 Pennington, R R, *Stannary Law: a History of the Mining Law of Cornwall and Devon* (Newton Abbot: David and Charles, 1973), pp160, 176, 214, 217; Todd, A C, pp71–81. The Wherry case was still being disputed by lawyers in June 1799 (see Torrens, H S, 'Some newly discovered letters from Jonathan Hornblower (1753–1815)', pp196–200). The fact that Cornish engineers of high repute regarded the Hornblower engine as superior (for whatever reason) is the crucial — if forgotten — point. The historiography of this Wherry trial is confused by Todd's misdating of a letter which he then wrongly takes to relate to the Wherry Arbitration when its true date (5 January 1799) shows it instead relates to the case then being tried in London over the validity of Watt's patent — see Torrens, H S, 'New light on the Hornblower and Winwood Compound Steam Engine', p35.
91 [Enys, J D], 'The President's address', *Journal of the Royal Institution of Cornwall*, 13 (1898), p15; Torrens, H S, 'Some newly discovered letters from Jonathan Hornblower (1753–1815)', p191
92 Anon., 'Dreadful accident', *Philosophical Magazine*, 16 (1803), p372
93 Torrens, H S, 'Some newly discovered letters from Jonathan Hornblower (1753–1815)', p199
94 Doldowlod archives — letters box, 'Account of premiums due from J Wilkinson charged to Jany 1796'; Williams, C J, *The Lead Mines of the Alyn Valley* (Hawarden: Flintshire Historical Society, 1987)
95 Torrens, H S, 'Some newly discovered letters from Jonathan Hornblower (1753–1815)', p195
96 Bowie, G, 'Early stationary steam engines in Ireland', *Industrial Archaeology Review*, 2 (1978), p171
97 Hadfield, C, *Thomas Telford's Temptation: Telford and William Jessop's Reputation* (Cleobury Mortimer: Baldwin, 1993)
98 Griffiths, J, *The Third Man: the Life and Times of William Murdoch* (London: Andre Deutsch, 1992)
99 Playfair, W, p580

The story of the story of the life of George Stephenson

Adrian Jarvis

It is well known that the popular image of George Stephenson is inflated. There are those who believe he invented the steam engine and some think that he invented the steam locomotive or was 'the first railway engineer'. Some of what is written about the life and work of George Stephenson is at best unreliable, sometimes fictitious, and occasionally the exact opposite of the truth. Comparing material which is contemporary, or very nearly so, with more recent writing we find marked discrepancies, nearly all tending to 'build up' George Stephenson, for which there appears to be no grounding in fact.

I shall employ a number of what might be termed 'yardstick errors' for assessing the veracity or otherwise of accounts of George Stephenson's life and works. Because I suspect that it is not axiomatic that these are false, I shall enumerate them and summarise the evidence for their falsehood.

Error 1. George Stephenson invented the blast pipe

Despite the plethora of opinion on this subject during the 'battle of the blast-pipe' it is not always recognised that George Stephenson is among the less probable candidates for its invention. Ironically, the confusion was mainly compounded by R Young,[1] whose motive was to show that Timothy Hackworth, not George Stephenson, was the true inventor. In fact, it is reasonably clear that the inventor would be the man who first discovered that exhausting steam into the chimney base improves combustion.[2] The question of who did or did not constrict the opening of the pipe, and by how much, is completely irrelevant. This was a red herring instigated by Young, which assumed that most readers would not realise (did Young realise?) that the optimum constriction of the blast pipe was determined, not by the degree of originality of the man applying it,[3] but by the ratio between the heating surface and the total cross-sectional area of the tubes. The smaller the relative tube area, the greater the benefit from a sharper blast; the larger it was (as in a single-flue locomotive), the less the benefit.[4] The point was simply the turning of the exhaust into the chimney in such a way as to draw the fire, which was done by Richard Trevithick.

Error 2. George Stephenson built, or at least designed, the Rocket

There is not a single contemporary document that proves any constructive input by George Stephenson to either the design or the construction of the *Rocket*. Nicholas Wood, who was, if anything, a witness biased in George Stephenson's favour, described the *Rocket* as entered for the Rainhill Trials by Robert Stephenson.[5] A contemporary poem makes it clear that George's role was to be proud of such a talented son.[6] The letters in which George allegedly told Robert how to do it do not survive, but the letters from Robert to Henry Booth do,[7] which may have caused the failure of some historians to distinguish between the designer of the *Rocket* and the proprietors of the *Rocket* to whom the premium was awarded. The proprietors were Booth and both Stephensons, but proprietors were not necessarily inventors, designers or constructors: they were simply the men who risked their money. There have been many misunderstandings here: Booth neither patented nor invented the multi-tubular boiler, which had been known in principle for some years.[8] George seems never to have appreciated, as Robert did, the benefit of a light, high-speed machine as a way of exerting more horsepower on an inadequate track. On the contrary, he seems to have viewed more power as being synonymous with more tractive effort, which brought with it the need for greater adhesive weight[9] and consequent track problems.

Error 3. George Stephenson invented the method of crossing Chat Moss

A number of canal engineers had carried embankments across bogs or mosses, notably James Brindley and William Jessop.[10] Before the Liverpool & Manchester Railway was enabled, William Roscoe built and operated a small tramroad system on the Moss.[11] The tales told about how no man could tread on the Moss and live are thus exaggerated. The contractor for building the line over the Moss had previously been Roscoe's agent, so we may suspect that it was Robert Stannard, not

George Stephenson, who solved the problem. Bailey went further, and suggested that Stephenson opposed the correct solution and insisted on perseverance in drainage works and tipping spoil.[12]

Error 4. George Stephenson exhibited a 'truly noble and manly character'

We are asked to believe that George Stephenson was possessed of such personal qualities that all those who met him could not fail to like and respect him.[13] The engineers with whom Stephenson quarrelled would fill a small biographical dictionary: William James, James Overton, both George and John Rennie, James Mills, Thomas Telford, Joseph Locke and C B Vignoles were just some of the multitude. The publication of Samuel Smiles' biography called forth some unusually splenetic responses.[14] The point made here does not relate to whether George was or was not responsible for any particular thing: merely that for one so apparently amiable, he upset an uncommon number of people, and was hounded beyond the grave by a succession of well-informed (if not entirely disinterested) authors.

Samuel Smiles' Life of George Stephenson

It has been customary to blame Samuel Smiles for most of the excesses and inaccuracies found in more recent works,[15] which are taken to be borrowed from him. It is true that at the beginning of this century there existed a genre of popular engineering publications which contained all the yardstick errors and more beside.[16] These certainly owed little to scholarly research and relied heavily on Smiles. The furious protests his book called forth may indicate that their writers foresaw that Smiles would have a great and continuing influence on the perception of his subject. While there is some truth in the accusation against Smiles, it needs qualification. None of the yardstick errors was first published by Smiles, although he gave them greater prominence by virtue of his commercial success. Later writers have not been slow to embroider Smiles' work, and in some cases to confuse and garble it, resulting in the introduction of new errors.

Smiles was given to writing informative prefaces to his work. That to the 1862 version, published as volume 3 of *Lives of the Engineers*, explains why and how he came to write the book. He enumerates a small number of existing printed works and concludes that 'the Life of George Stephenson, therefore, remained to be written'. In one sense that was clearly true, for the works he mentions are fairly slight, as are some others which he does not mention. On the other hand, there were other short accounts available which, in their different ways, provided virtually all the essential ingredients of what would become the popular view of George Stephenson for a century.

If one were researching George Stephenson *de novo*, an obvious place to start would be the *Proceedings of the Institution of Mechanical Engineers*, where there would be his obituary, as the Institution's first president. There is indeed a fairly extensive memoir written by John Scott Russell.[17] Smiles does not mention or refer to it at all. It may be, as he states, that James Kitson was the man who first suggested (in 1848) that Smiles should write the life of George Stephenson,[18] but the suggestion that *someone* should do so was also made in 1848 by Scott Russell:

> . . . but I cannot conclude without expressing an earnest wish that his life as a man, exhibiting the beauty and excellence of his life in all its cheering aspects [be written] . . . This would be a most valuable and instructive work . . . to see justice done to the memory of one of England's greatest men, the founder of our railway system and of the Institution of Mechanical Engineers.

Scott Russell's *Memoir* does not contain all the yardstick errors. We do read, however, that George Stephenson was the 'first constructor and chief inventor of Locomotives and Railways', a statement in need of severe qualification.

Error 4 is also present: 'If he could hate an enemy, he never masked his antipathy by hypocrisy; but he was a warm and earnest friend.' While we may admit that E M S Paine sometimes allowed emotion to overcome her, the documents referred to in her books and in F R Dodds' articles about William James,[19] suggest that this is scarcely true. There is much else in Scott Russell's *Memoir* which is doubtful: George Stephenson was a lone dreamer, we are told, who foresaw locomotive speeds of '10, 20, 50 and 100 miles an hour, and who had recently determined to do it'. According to Smiles, Stephenson specifically opposed high speeds, and considered anything above forty miles per hour to be uneconomical, dangerous and altogether unnecessary.[20]

I may appear to 'debunk' the reputation of George

Stephenson, and such inflated claims have been made for him that this is almost inevitable. It is, therefore, only fair to remark on one error in the *Memoir* where George Stephenson appears to be denied the credit justly his. Scott Russell explains that Stephenson adopted the fish-bellied rail but that he stopped short of making it in sections with joints only at 'every fifth or sixth chair', and continued to use single sections with a joint at every chair. In fact the Liverpool & Manchester Railway used exactly the form of rail which Scott Russell stated it should have.

The Institution of Civil Engineers could not publish a memoir of a non-member, but Joshua Field's presidential address of 16 January 1849 effectively contained one.[21] Field principally promulgated errors 1 and 2. Early locomotives used a single flue with a short chimney 'upon which the fire wholly depended for its draught'. He went on to explain that without some great new development, the locomotive engine would have remained a slow, lumbering device suitable only for freight. The breakthrough came in the combination of the blast-pipe and the tubular boiler: 'This important and admirable combination was designed and executed by Mr [George] Stephenson' although it was conceded that Robert Stephenson also played an important part.

Anyone familiar with the Smiles ideology of self-help would expect obituaries of George Stephenson to appear in journals associated with the education and improvement of the working classes. *The Odd-Fellows' Magazine* contains an example,[22] but it does not live up to our expectations, concerning itself primarily with George Stephenson not as a self-made man, but rather as a mechanical genius. The locomotive works of Robert Stephenson & Co. was established by George 'in partnership with his son and two other persons, which still exists under the name of . . .', clearly implying that when it was established it had some other name. At the Rainhill Trials, 'Mr Stephenson [George] entered the lists as a competitor and his celebrated engine *The Rocket* [sic] won for him the prize.' Error 4 is also present: 'His natural benevolence of disposition endeared him to all around . . .'.

A less obvious pre-Smiles account of George Stephenson, and one which amply exhibits the message missing from *The Odd-Fellows' Magazine*, is that by J R Leifchild, which appeared when Smiles was in the later stages of preparing his work.[23] All the outline of George's early life, which Smiles was to make so familiar, is there, including a number of the favourite anecdotes and supposed quotations, such as his declaration that his wage of twelve shillings at Walbottle Pit 'made him a man for life'. Errors 2, 3 and 4 are present and the description 'railway engineer of the earliest railways' implies error 1.

By the time the first edition of Smiles appeared, there was, therefore, a tradition of untruthful and inaccurate biography of George Stephenson. In seeking an explanation, we may begin with Leifchild. Smiles, in his introduction, claims that he gained a great deal of authentic information from people who had worked with George Stephenson in his early life. It was important, says Smiles, to carry out the work before all those who remembered him had died. Leifchild revealed his pride in the achievements of a fellow Geordie with the statement that 'It is always a subject of boasting amongst the Newcastle miners, that their trams and their mechanisms furnished the thoughts and plans for railways, and this principally through Geordie [Stephenson]'.[24] In other words, it is eminently possible that some of the anecdotes used by Leifchild and Smiles, and all who followed them, were invented in miners' boasting during their drinking sessions, and had evolved into local folk tales.

Smiles was not always as gullible and uncritical as some would have us believe. Leifchild includes a tale of the young George Stephenson seeking the hand of Miss Hindmarsh, the daughter of a 'respectable farmer', who would not have the humble engineman for a son-in-law. 'Since Miss would not have him, he descended one step and asked her servant. The said servant had sense enough to accept Geordie, and a good wife she was.' Later, 'she died, and George again made up to Miss Hindmarsh, the farmer's daughter. This time she was wise, and became his wife; and she did live to see and share in her husband's honours and wealth.' This story did not ring true with Smiles: he checked it with the Hindmarsh family, found it to be untrue and included a lengthy footnote (in some editions) explaining its falsehood. He could not resist pointing out that Leifchild had drawn this story from a short sketch of George Stephenson's life in *Eliza Cook's Journal*,[25] which he, Smiles, had written 'on imperfect information, and before he had the opportunity of thoroughly sifting, as he has since done, the facts of George Stephenson's early life'.

In another respect, Smiles could be gullible. There are two main printed sources for his account of the crucial period of George Stephenson's career from his first locomotive-building ventures at Killingworth to the opening of the Liverpool & Manchester Railway. They are Nicholas Wood's *Practical Treatise on Railroads* and Henry Booth's *An Account of the Liverpool and Manchester Railway.*[26] It is well known that Wood's work was censored in the interests of building the image of George Stephenson, and that Booth had numerous reasons, both personal and corporate, for doing the same.[27] Between them, these two writers introduced all the yardstick errors and some others as well. Booth, for example, told of George's ordeal in giving evidence for the 1825 Bill while concealing the reason for it, namely that the estimates and survey had not been correctly prepared. He chose instead to portray the issue as a gladiatorial conflict between the forces of progress and of reactionary vested interest, a misinterpretation adopted by many writers ever since.[28]

At this point we must consider what we mean by a contemporary source. Contemporary material does not, strictly, include afterthoughts or reminiscences. However near the action the writer was, he was capable of looking at the past in a rose-tinted mirror. C Hadfield has shown us that the formerly irreproachable Thomas Telford did this,[29] and there is little doubt that George Stephenson and his fellow travellers did it too. That is not to say that reminiscence is necessarily false or misleading, indeed it may be valid and extremely informative, but it does not automatically deserve the special credibility of contemporary evidence, and should be treated with caution.

It seems clear that some of these early reminiscences were limited in their value by the demon drink. The first time George Stephenson was described as 'the inventor of the locomotive' was in an after-dinner speech.[30] Many of George's own utterances on the subject of his early career were made in circumstances which might be considered to lack academic rigour. On the subject of locomotive speeds, for example, he once had to admit that it was true that he had said that a speed of 100 mph was possible, but added that he had never said it was desirable. It is not hard to picture George swaying slightly between the toast to the father of railways and the beginning of his proposal of the toast to the shareholders of a railway company. During such a proposal, speeds might easily rise to 100 mph — or more.[31] Smiles' assertions of George's habitual temperance were probably little better founded than those he entered on behalf of another notoriously drunken genius, namely James Brindley.[32] This is not in any way a smear on George: becoming inebriated in the later stages of a celebration dinner was perfectly acceptable conduct in a gentleman at the time. Edward Pease went further in his diary, alleging that George was a habitual drunkard. Whether that was strictly true is immaterial; it confirms that there was a likelihood of inaccurate reminiscences being circulated.[33]

Whether Smiles knew about George Stephenson's drinking is unclear. Given his experience both as a newspaper editor and as a railway company secretary he was probably aware of the nature of opening celebrations. What is important is that he accepted evidence, the credibility of which was almost certainly tainted by drink, and then, to make George appear a gentleman by the changed standards of the late 1850s, concealed that taint from his readers. The result, whether intended or not, has been the misleading of more than a few of his followers. Neither should we forget the audiences to which such speeches were delivered. Shareholders had anxiously sat out a long period of construction, usually watching the overspend accumulate, and now had the prospect of some return on their capital. Directors had battled their way through years of often difficult negotiations to obtain an Act, acquire land and get the line built. Engineers and contractors had faced all manner of problems and worked day and night to overcome them. Local manufacturers and businessmen had eagerly looked forward to the day when their ventures would benefit from the new line. Everyone, in short, was enjoying a massive release of tension and was thus in the mood to celebrate. It was certainly not the occasion to query a claim to credit or merit, and the contents of speeches would be recounted to unsuspecting third parties, including Smiles, long after the euphoria had evaporated.[34]

The nature of mid-nineteenth-century truth

At one level, it is axiomatic that gentlemen tell the truth. To accuse John Scott Russell, J R Leifchild, or any of the others mentioned above of lying would have been unthinkable. The historian must be careful to weigh the different ethical standards of past ages before coming to ill-informed judgements.

Scott Russell's account includes some very curious statements:

It will be recorded, that about the middle of the nineteenth century Locomotives began to run upon railways, and that George Stephenson, the President of the Institution of Mechanical Engineers, was the man to whose original genius chiefly the world was indebted for the discovery.[35]

It is clear that Scott Russell knew that the pioneering, or 'discovery', phase of the railways lasted from about 1800 to 1830. He cannot have thought that describing George Stephenson as the 'first constructor of Locomotives and Railways' was accurate.[36] He went on to explain how 'the foundation of our Society was an act most appropriate to the termination of a career so arduous and successful,' and how 'one of the great objects of our Society is the encouragement of mechanical invention' which would spare the rising generation from the difficulties George Stephenson had faced when 'the unhappy moments of his youth were those in which his inventions encountered the opposition of prejudice and interest' on account of their novelty.

The last meeting George Stephenson attended was held on 26 July 1848, when he read a paper entitled 'On the fallacies of the rotary engine'.[37] He explained that there was 'no power but in the lever' and that the engine there exhibited by a Mr Onion could not work. When Onion provided evidence that it not only could, but did, George was having none of it: 'The engine might have answered at one trial, but it might fail at the next.' It was a rather dogmatic performance by the president, perhaps what one might expect from an elderly man of great achievement faced with something unconventional. The previous meeting had heard a paper by J E McConnell in which he showed that imbalance in locomotive wheels not only caused poor riding but also measurable waste of power. If George had been receptive to new ideas, would he not have seen the potential benefit of the better balance of a rotary engine? He 'really could not see anything of value in it'.

This passage is directly contrary to what Scott Russell wrote and it is most unlikely that he was unaware of the castigation of Mr Onion and his fallacies. Why, then, did he write what he did? Was it just a question of a white lie in the usual good cause of honouring the recently departed? These are not merely rhetorical questions upon whose answers we can only speculate, for after Scott Russell had read his *Memoir*, there followed a formal proposal to minute the regret of the members at the loss of their president. Mr Geach, proposing, provided an answer, which deserves quotation *in extenso*.

He would quite allow that his manners were sometimes rough; he would quite allow that there were peculiarities in his character, which had to be considered as peculiarities: but he was quite sure that those who knew him best considered that these very peculiarities gave him a greater claim on their regard. He was willing to allow that he had seen in Mr Stephenson what in other men might subject them to criticism; but when it came from Mr Stephenson it came from a privileged person.[38]

Geach is saying simply that when reminiscing about George Stephenson people are not concerned with fact *and that there is no reason why they should be.* Scott Russell had not been lying or concealing the truth but writing what it was proper to write about a privileged person and not about others. He had written that which he knew to be factually incorrect, but which was, in a sense, true.

It was an age in which neo-medievalism was rampant in poetry, literature, architecture and the decorative arts, and incipient in music.[39] The religious revival which animated both the right and the left of the Church of England (leaving the centre happily ensconced in the living of Bray) was gradually creating a working replica of the 'Christocentric Society' perceived as having existed in the Middle Ages. In the process, the place of logic and demonstrable fact *vis-à-vis* that of faith could, and did, change. Geach's statement is not far, in logical terms, from this: 'It is not permitted to us, who have received these bones, to be troubled by doubts about them.' R W Southern, commenting on this and other extracts, remarks that

The monastic forgeries of this age cannot be understood unless allowance is made for the sanctity of corporate traditions — sometimes like 'age-old' custom itself, of recent growth — which outweighed all consideration of what we should call facts.[40]

These extracts relate, of course, to twelfth-century England. But is it stretching imagination too far to suggest that Geach and Scott Russell were part of a corporate tradition, that their age-old custom was of recent growth (two years) and that there were considerations which outweighed what we would call facts? If so, then they could indeed accept things which were without factual foundation: 'I confess that I have nowhere read this, but so many reputable men assert that it happened, that I believe it would be a great impudence not to believe it.'[41] I have met engineers who regarded any questioning of the George Stephenson myth as a personal affront.

This was a historical minefield. Here were people going on the record with what appeared to be facts, but which were actually pious utterances of doctrine — the doctrine of the privilege of George Stephenson. They were writing from positions of authenticity — they knew, or worked with the subject — and their writings were very nearly contemporary. They were, in short, eminently credible yet deeply flawed.

It would be patronising to suggest that Smiles blundered unknowingly into this minefield and suffered the consequences. On the contrary, his barely hidden agenda in writing the life of George Stephenson caused him to lay a few extra mines of his own. From a wide variety of sources, many of them partial, unreliable or even by today's standards mendacious, he produced a masterpiece of biography. If it lacked the philosophical power of Carlyle, the literary capability of Dickens or the scholarship of Macaulay, it had a little of each. It sold well, it was demonstrably well researched, it had no serious competitor, and it therefore passed into the canon without any very careful assessment.[42] The results have been, in historiographical terms, quite amazing. Until very recently, even respected scholars in notoriously rigorous fields like economic history have been willing to go back as far as Smiles and treat him as source material, without feeling the need to go back any further. (That, incidentally, is why the £5 note pictures George Stephenson with Robert Stephenson's *Rocket*, Robert's *Active* and Ignatius Bonomi's bridge: the Bank of England's researchers saw no need to go further back than Smiles either.)

The followers of Samuel Smiles

Samuel Smiles had put in a prodigious amount of work on George Stephenson, and such writers never lack followers anxious to pay them the compliment of imitation. The trouble was that many of them did not even plagiarise accurately. Charles Francis Adams Jr,[43] for example, pays tribute to Smiles on page one and, on the same page, he also describes George Stephenson as the inventor of the locomotive, a claim Smiles specifically repudiated. Because Adams was writing in America we may assume that the edition of Smiles which he had partly read was American. The American editions of Smiles give far greater credit to other early locomotive builders, especially Richard Trevithick, than did the English ones.[44] He goes on to complain of Smiles taking liberty with facts, particularly with reference to his failure to realise the cataclysmic nature of the invention of the locomotive, which 'burst rather than stole or crept upon the world'. The facts presented by Smiles show a development from 1804 to 1829, a rather slow-peak burst, but fact does not seem to have weighed too heavily on Adams' mind.

If we were to believe Smiles, that is all one could expect of Americans, whom he characterised as plagiarists and copyright pirates almost to a man.[45] But such a lack of academic rigour is more surprising in a Cambridge Professor of Economic History, L C A Knowles. 'It is well known that the first attempt to get the Liverpool & Manchester Bill through Parliament failed because a noble Duke said it would spoil his fox covers . . .'.[46] This is a garbled and half-understood plagiarism from Smiles. The Bill for the building of the Stockton & Darlington Railway was obstructed by the Duke of Cleveland. Smiles, a veteran of the Anti-Corn Law League, did not fail to characterise the Duke of Cleveland as a worthless blimp standing in the way of progress. By the 1920s, such prejudices might have been tempered by scholarly investigation. So far was this from the case that Knowles absorbed and passed on the 'message' while neglecting to transcribe correctly the facts to support it. No duke and no fox covers were involved in the building of the Liverpool & Manchester Railway. According to Henry Booth, the Earls of Derby and Sefton thought that 'the sanctity of their domains would be invaded and the privacy of their residences destroyed'.[47] Adams and Knowles had both taken Smiles' account and added to it fresh inaccuracies.

Smiles knew that it was William Hedley who proved that iron wheels would provide traction on iron rails, but J F Layson felt it necessary to claim this discovery for George Stephenson.[48] It made a good story for explaining the Blenkinsop rack-rail without requiring any understanding of adhesive weight and the problems it brought in terms of fragile cast-iron track. That may be why Layson claimed that Trevithick's Pen-y-Darren locomotive was 'found to be defective in principle, and was in consequence abandoned'. Over what the defective principle was, a veil is drawn: no evidence is entered against Smiles' assertion that 'she worked very well, but frequently, from her weight, broke the tram-plates . . .'.[49] Evidence to support Layson against Smiles on this point is still lacking.

The publications prompted by the centenaries of the Robert Stephenson & Co. works and the Stockton & Darlington and Liverpool & Manchester Railways were, in the main, of a higher standard, if only because they dwelled less on the human interest of George Stephenson's rise to fame and fortune.[50] Contemporary as they were with J H Jackman's *The Development of Transportation in Modern England,* C E R Sherrington's *The Economics of Rail Transport in Britain* and J H Clapham's *An Economic History of Modern Britain,* we might assume that a new age of careful, critical and dispassionate history had arrived. So, in a way, it had, but Rome was not built in a day. Sherrington, for example, follows Smiles' view that 'in 1815 [George] Stephenson produced the prototype of the modern locomotive' or, to put it another way, 'It may in fact be regarded as the type of the present locomotive engine.'[51] Clapham does not question that George Stephenson was responsible for the *Rocket*.[52] A P Fleming and H J Brocklehurst, writing in 1925, credit George with building the *Rocket,* 'conceiving' the crossing of Chat Moss and state that William James 'gave up'.[53] By this time, a thorough and critical reading of the *secondary* literature would have established the need for very careful investigation of these points.

Nor did C F Dendy Marshall *et al.* prove to be the first gleam of a new dawn; there were plenty of errors yet to come. Eminent economic historians continued to borrow from historians of engineering, who in turn borrowed from Smiles. T S Ashton, for example, explains how George Stephenson 'increased the draught to the firebox',[54] a statement which implies a limited understanding of the working of a locomotive, while P Mathias claims for George that he established that the friction of an iron wheel on an iron rail was quite sufficient.[55] This provides the useful information that Mathias was using a pre-1862 edition of Smiles, as the mistake was corrected in that and later ones.[56]

It is understandable that economic historians might follow, relatively uncritically, people they regard as specialists in engineering history. Another aspect of the Stephenson story is that of deliberate invention. Smiles gave a brief account of the confrontation between George Stephenson and Ned Nelson, the 'works bully' at Black Callerton Colliery, which culminated in a fight which George won. Nelson was much the stronger man and George had never fought before, but triumphed through a combination of wiry strength, agility and intelligence.[57] When J Rowland takes up the story, Smiles' modest narrative expands to over five pages, enhanced with details of individual blows and their effects, and written as if by an eye-witness.[58] Some might interpret this as an application of the standard story of Jack the Giant Killer, but in fact it was neither invented gratuitously nor plagiarised to pad out the story. It was invented as evidence for events to be brought out later in the book, an altogether more pernicious procedure.[59]

The 1825 Liverpool & Manchester Railway Bill

The cumulative effect of repetition of the errors mentioned above, and others for which there is no space in this paper, was to create an image of an engineer quite beyond the run of ordinary mortals. From that, it followed that when he was involved in a gross failure, the fault must lie elsewhere. The loss of the first Liverpool & Manchester Bill was certainly a gross failure, and we find some of George Stephenson's apologists producing excuses worthy of Billy Bunter.

First, we are told that there were uncommon difficulties in making the survey owing to the reactionary and anti-social refusal of landowners to allow surveying on their property, and that this was one of the reasons why the survey proved woefully inaccurate: you cannot make an accurate survey furtively, in the dark, with gamekeepers shooting at you.[60] We may begin by doubting the alleged shooting: most gamekeepers were handier with a gun than George Stephenson proved to be with a theodolite, yet no-one appears to have been injured. Far more important is the fact that there is no reason why landowners should welcome surveyors, even those who had the decency to seek permission, which in several instances George's men did not. In 1825 there was no railway working in a manner or at a speed fundamentally different from those of a canal, and every landowner knew that boatmen included a noticeable minority of expert thieves and poachers. Only firm evidence that the new railway would work at high speed and without stopping between stations would affect their view, and such evidence could not be given in 1825.

Behind the opprobrium extended to the landowners lies an acceptance of the conventional parliamentary fiction that canals, railways, docks and other such works were undertaken for the benefit of the public. They were not: they were undertaken to make a profit for their promoters. There was nothing wrong with that, but it does not entitle George Stephenson or anybody else to a season ticket for the moral high ground. The fact that railways later became a great public benefit is not material: neither the promoters nor the landowners knew that in 1825. In short, to blame the inaccuracy of the survey on landowners is patently unjust and was produced as an excuse. It may be recalled that these stories were first given currency by Henry Booth who was of Whiggish views and also stood to gain a great deal from the railway.

The canal proprietors have consistently been portrayed as a malign vested interest.[61] As with the landowners, there is absolutely no reason why they should not have behaved as they did. Their duty was to the shareholders and they would have been acting irresponsibly if they had betrayed their interests in favour of some vacuous notion of public benefit. As C Hadfield and G Biddle pointed out, much of the evidence for the railway was inaccurate, even mendacious, on the subject of the canals.[62]

The 'canal interest' is blamed for the supposedly dastardly deed of employing Mr Alderson, the counsel who destroyed George Stephenson's evidence. Even relatively balanced accounts like L T C Rolt's give Alderson a moderately bad press.[63] Smiles' account of the proceedings of the Committee is one of the least reliable parts of his work, and others have not been slow to follow him, or, indeed, to 'improve' on him. Central to all these accounts is the idea that George was a self-taught genius who had difficulty in explaining himself and who suffered the added disadvantage of a strong Northumbrian accent, so that his engineering skills were discredited by a man whose only merit was a slick way with words. His difficulties were accentuated, it has been suggested, by established but mediocre engineers 'ganging up on him' and giving stupid evidence which detracted from his visionary plan. Francis Giles did indeed miscalculate the cost of the Chat Moss works, but William Cubitt, who was asked to check Stephenson's levels and found not a single one of them correct, appears to have been right. George Stephenson's isolation looks more like that of Thomas Telford, brought about by a reluctance to work with his peers.[64]

There is a simple way of discovering the truth of the Alderson accusations: it is to look at his questioning of other witnesses. Neither John Rastrick nor Nicholas Wood went to Eton and Kings, and neither was among the imaginary Corinthians of the Institution. Yet their evidence was not harmed in the least by Alderson; indeed, on one occasion, Rastrick rather discomforted the 'villain'.[65] If we approach the issue without a preconception of the infallibility of George Stephenson the difference in the examinations becomes clear. Rastrick and Wood were speaking on matters of which they had prolonged, personal, hands-on experience. George was speaking of work done by others and it is that difference which Alderson clinically, and entirely correctly, exposed.

The results in historiographical terms have been remarkable. According to J Rowland, 'No engineer, and an uneducated one at that, could be expected to outwit the cleverest lawyers of the day', and George Stephenson 'is not to be blamed, however, for the failure of this attempt'.[66] F Ferneyhough is more judicious, but still writes: 'Though he had been made to look a fool, he was no man's fool, just not a man of tongues. Of such meagre literacy, it is astonishing that he had survived the ordeal at all.'[67] L T C Rolt made no attempt to conceal the fact that the destruction of George's evidence was a major cause of the failure of the Bill, but his lack of the 'ability to counter their quicker wits' was an extenuating circumstance and his failure was 'Through his mistakes in detail'[68]— detail such as a credible estimate of the cost of the line or the location of the datum level.

By 1980, R E Carlson and R H G Thomas had each published new scholarly histories of the railway as a whole.[69] The former includes an extensive account of the Committee proceedings. Neither work seeks to make any excuse for George Stephenson's poor performance, nor to suggest that he had not failed in one of the key duties of a chief engineer. At last, Smiles had been laid to rest by a careful and open-minded scrutiny of the source material. But it was not to be: the traditional version of George Stephenson was far too resilient, and in 1981 we find J T van Riemsdijk writing of:

> the constant attempts to undermine the route selected, of the introduction of other engineers at crucial moments in the debate who might conceivably undermine [George] Stephenson's authority, and to jibes about his professional standing. Stephenson was as solid as a rock. He knew he understood the business of railway construction better than anybody else, but he was not arrogant. He was just immovable.[70]

A gloomy prognosis

The essential facts of the life of George Stephenson are, as might be expected for such a prominent figure, fairly easy to find from contemporary sources. Between about 1830 and 1848 we find additions to, and fundamental distortions of, the story appearing, so that few of Samuel Smiles' errors were of his own making. Smiles has dominated the story since 1857, and while we can identify many works which weed out errors, the weeds always grow again, sometimes ranker, more varied and more numerous than before.

The newly competitive world in which museums and kindred bodies now find themselves will inhibit any change in this situation: it is a curious fact that it is still the names of Smiles' engineers that 'sell'. That is why works of William Jessop will continue to be credited to Thomas Telford and the *Rocket* will be 'George Stephenson's *Rocket*'. George Stephenson was a good thing for the early railway industry and a good thing for Samuel Smiles — which he continues to be today.

Acknowledgements

My thanks to National Museums and Galleries on Merseyside for time in which to write and to travel; to Victoria Haworth for much helpful discussion of ideas and several references; to Douglas Braid, sadly prevented by ill-health from contributing to the conference, for the reference in note 42 and for the associated remark 'One year's weeds, seven years' seeds', which sums up the whole subject rather succinctly.

Notes and references

1 Young, R, *Timothy Hackworth and the Locomotive* (Shildon: Shildon 'Stockton & Darlington Railway' Jubilee Committee, 1975), reprint of 1923 edn. Chapter 6 chronicles the 'Battle' — of which it is itself a part.

2 Trevithick did not publish on the subject, but see Dickinson, H W and Titley, A, *Richard Trevithick* (Cambridge: Cambridge University Press, 1934), pp65–66, for a transcript of part of Trevithick's letter of 4 March 1804 in which he mentions his observation to his friend and mentor Davies Giddy.

3 Young, R, pp222–29, makes much of the difference between an 'eduction pipe' and a blast pipe.

4 Which is why Nicholas Wood recounts the removal of the blast pipe at Killingworth (Wood, N, *A Practical Treatise on Rail-roads* (London: Knight & Lacey, 1825), p293).

5 Wood, N, p363

6 A facsimile appears in Thomas, R H G, *The Liverpool & Manchester Railway* (London: Batsford, 1980), p74: 'And loudly tell to all around, How Robert beat them a'. His father too, mechanic's pride, May proudly boast a son so clever . . .'.

7 An interesting example of 2 + 2 = 5. There *are* letters on a variety of engineering topics, and Robert Stephenson's letters to Henry Booth read like responses to letters from George Stephenson. But George's letters, or at least those that survive, do not contain any constructive design input to the *Rocket* as built, and Robert's letters to Booth represent his accounting for the money which Booth was putting into the project. For Booth's alleged part, see Booth, H, *Henry Booth 1789–1869* (Ilfracombe: A H Stockwell Ltd, 1980), chapter 5.

8 For Samuel Smiles' reservations, see Smiles, S, *The Life of George Stephenson* (New York: Harper, 1868), pp318–19. The differences between what Smiles wrote in England and in America are considered in Jarvis, A, 'Engineering the image: the lessening of Samuel Smiles', *Journal of the Railway and Canal Historical Society*, 31 (1993), p176.

9 See letter, George Stephenson to Robert Stephenson, 23 February 1827, where the new locomotive design for the Liverpool & Manchester Railway 'will be a nuge [huge] job . . . you will think I have mistaken some ideas about this, but I think not . . .', transcribed in Skeat, W O, *George Stephenson: the Engineer and his Letters* (London: Institution of Mechanical Engineers, 1973), p103. The *Rocket*, was not, of course, a 'nuge job'.

10 Brindley crossed Sale Moor with the Bridgewater canal; Jessop the Great Bog of Allen with the Grand Canal.

11 Bailey, W H, 'A new chapter in the history of

the Manchester & Liverpool [sic] Railway', *Transactions of the Manchester Association of Engineers* (1889), pp23–29

12 This is partly corroborated by the fact that George Stephenson's alleged explanation to the 1825 Parliamentary Committee (see note 64), of how he would 'float' the road, simply does not exist. It is what Rackham (note 42) would call a 'factoid'.

13 Smiles, S, *Lives of the Engineers* (New York: Augustus Kelley, 1968), reprint of 1862 edn, I, p189

14 The most hate-filled was probably Paine, E M S, *The Two James's and the Two Stephensons* (London: 1861), but Hedley, O D, *Who Invented the Locomotive Engine?* (London: 1859), was not exactly friendly to Smiles' work: 'abounding as it does with statements so worthless and facts so fictitious . . .', p81.

15 For example Malet, H, *Bridgewater, the Canal Duke* (Manchester: Manchester University Press, 1977), pxii, attributing historiographical problems to 'the popularity of Smiles' biased and inaccurate but persuasive prose'.

16 For example Layson, J F, *Great Engineers* (London: S W Partridge, n.d. [*c*1895]); Holmes, F H, *Great Works by Great Men* (London: n.d. [*c*1904])

17 *Proceedings of the Institution of Mechanical Engineers* (October 1848), pp1–13

18 Smiles, S, *Lives of the Engineers*, III, pvii

19 Paine, E M S; Dodds, F R, 'Was Stephenson the father of railways?', *Railway Magazine*, V (July–December 1899), pp33–42, and 'The father of railways', pp364–68

20 Smiles, S, *Lives of the Engineers*, III, pp364–65

21 *Minutes of the Proceedings of the Institution of Civil Engineers*, VIII (1849), pp28–32

22 *The Odd-Fellows' Magazine* (Grand United Order, 1850), p44. The magazine had been reorganised, which accounts for the delay in publication.

23 Leifchild, J R, *Our Coal and Our Coal Pits* (London: 1856), pp228–40

24 Leifchild, J R, p229

25 Smiles, S, *Lives of the Engineers*, III, p158–60. The story was omitted later. Jeaffreson gives a different version again, which was adopted almost verbatim by Rolt, L T C, *George and Robert Stephenson* (Harmondsworth: Pelican, 1978), pp8–9, 17. See also *Eliza Cook's Journal*, I, no. 5 (1849), pp65–67. Skeat, W O, p38, exhumes the frog-kissing fairytale in the original form — as repudiated by its inventor.

26 Published, respectively, London (1825) and Liverpool (1830).

27 Rolt, L T C, p104. Booth not only invested in the *Rocket*, but was a key figure in the finance and management of the railway. In such a position you 'built up' the engineer.

28 Further consideration is given to this issue below.

29 Hadfield, C, *Thomas Telford's Temptation* (Kidderminster: M & M Baldwin, 1993)

30 A famous occasion: 18 June 1844, George Hudson was in the chair and 350 guests celebrated the opening of the Darlington & Newcastle line. Sir Thomas Liddell made the claim for George Stephenson, who, in a long speech, did not repudiate it. Jeaffreson, J C, *The Life of Robert Stephenson, FRS* (London: Longman, Green, Reader & Dyer, 1866), I, p258.

31 The best known example is the dinner at Dunchurch, which lasted from 5.30 pm to around 8.00 am. George Stephenson apparently occupied the chair from 2.00–4.00 am (Rolt, L T C, p244).

32 Malet, H, p56

33 Lambert alleges that George had a standard speech for these occasions: Lambert, R S, *The Railway King* (London: G Allen & Unwin, 1934), p110. The implication is that it could be delivered on auto-pilot.

34 It may be that the usurpation of Jessop's works which forms the main theme of Hadfield, C, *Thomas Telford's Temptation*, was aided by the fact that Jessop habitually absented himself from such functions.

35 Scott Russell, J, *Proceedings of the Institution of Mechanical Engineers* (October 1848), p2

36 As Jeaffreson remarks, Liddell was also speaking with complete disregard for facts of which he could not be unaware.

37 *Proceedings of the Institution of Mechanical Engineers* (July 1848), pp1–5

38 *Proceedings of the Institution of Mechanical Engineers* (October 1848), p14

39 Girouard, M, *The Return to Camelot* (London: Yale University Press, 1981)

40 Southern, R W, *St Anselm and his Biographer* (Cambridge: Cambridge University Press, 1963), pp278–79

41 Southern, R W, p278

42 This sounds strange, following references to

Paine and Hedley, but the fact is that their outbursts *did not* bring about careful assessment. 'Pseudo-history is not killed by publishing real history. In a rational world, this might lead to controversy in which either the new version was accepted or the old version was shown to be true after all. In our world, the matter is not controversial: either the old version is re-told as if nothing had happened, or authors try to combine the two versions as though both could be true at once.' (Rackham, O, *Trees and Woodland in the British Landscape* (London: Dent, 1976), p23). For another example, see note 25.

43 Adams, C F Jr, *Railroads: their Origins and Problems* (London: G P Putnam & Sons, 1893), pp1–4

44 The Harper edition of Smiles has a useful biographical essay on Trevithick (see note 8). Post-1864 English editions are better than earlier ones in this respect.

45 Mackay, T (ed), *The Autobiography of Samuel Smiles LLD* (London: Murray, 1905), pp223–24

46 Knowles, L C A, *Industrial and Commercial Revolutions* (London: Routledge, 1926), p255

47 Booth, H, p17

48 Layson, J F, p17

49 Smiles, S, *Lives of the Engineers*, III, p83

50 Including Warren, J G H, *A Century of Locomotive Building* (Newcastle-upon-Tyne: 1923); Dendy Marshall, C F, *A History of British Locomotives down to the End of the Year 1831* (London: Oxford University Press, 1938); Dendy Marshall, C F, *Centenary History of the Liverpool & Manchester Railway* (London: Locomotive Publishing Co., 1930)

51 Sherrington, C E R, *The Economics of Rail Transport in Great Britain* (London: 1928), I, p167; Smiles, S, *Lives of the Engineers*, III,p103

52 Clapham, J H, *An Economic History of Modern Britain* (Cambridge: Cambridge University Press, 1950), I, p31

53 Fleming, A P and Brocklehurst, H J, *A History of Engineering* (London: A & C Black, 1925), pp155, 157–58

54 Ashton, T S, *The First Industrial Revolution 1760–1850* (Oxford: Oxford University Press, 1968), p70. On the following page we learn that '[George] Stephenson's *Rocket* won the competition at Rainhill'.

55 Mathias, P, *The First Industrial Nation* (London: Methuen, 1969), p278

56 From 1862 when produced as volume 3 of *Lives of the Engineers*, and from 1864 as the separate *Life of George Stephenson.*

57 Smiles, S, *Lives of the Engineers*, III, pp35–36

58 Rowland, J, *George Stephenson* (Watford: 1954), pp45–50

59 Which is admitted: 'the way in which he could turn an opponent's strength into weakness was something used again and again in George Stephenson's later career'. (Rowland, J, p50).

60 Present in numerous accounts, e.g. Rowland, J, p176.

61 For example, in Smiles, S, *Lives of the Engineers*, III, pp194–97.

62 Hadfield, C and Biddle, G, *Canals of the North West* (Newton Abbot: 1970), I. Chapter 5 presents a view of the Liverpool & Manchester Railway unfamilar to many railway historians.

63 For example, 'he [George] knew that Alderson and the opposition engineers had talked a great deal more nonsense than he had done . . .' (Rolt, L T C, p112).

64 Hadfield, C, pp8–9, 164–65. It is sometimes forgotten (conveniently) that Cubitt, who found George Stephenson's levels wrong, was not hired by the objectors, but as a last-ditch attempt at damage control by the Company.

65 *Proceedings of the Committee of the House of Commons on the Liverpool and Manchester Railroad Bill* (London: 1825). On p174, Alderson was corrected by a member of the Committee. Wood's evidence is on pp215–17.

66 Rowland, J, p184

67 Ferneyhough, F, *Liverpool & Manchester Railway 1830–1980* (London: 1980), p23

68 Rolt, L T C, p112

69 Carlson, R E, *The Liverpool & Manchester Railway Project 1821–31* (New York: 1969); Thomas R H G, p74

70 van Riemsdijk, J T, 'The hero as engineer', *Proceedings of the Institution of Mechanical Engineers*, 195 (1981), pp261–69, on p265. If, in the course of discussion of this paper, it had emerged that most of my references were false, would it be a virtue for me to remain 'just immovable'?

Samuel Smiles and the nineteenth-century novel

Simon Dentith

The following account is not primarily an exercise in debunking. I have to confess that it started out that way. Nineteenth-century notions of engineering, in their popular forms, seemed to me to be combined of magic and ideology in about equal measure — and indeed I still think that is part of the story. But I no longer think that it is the whole story, and I am like the fools in Oliver Goldsmith's poem, who came to scoff but remained to pray. My reading of Samuel Smiles' engineering biographies in particular, which will furnish the majority of my examples, now makes them seem to me to be altogether more interesting and substantial.

Nevertheless, my method remains similar to that which would have characterised my discarded enterprise in debunking. I hope to tease out the network of meanings in which the lives of engineers are told and retold, in a number of nineteenth-century writings, both 'fictional' and 'non-fictional'. I put these two categories in scare quotes because my way of reading tends to make the categorical difference between fiction and non-fiction seem relatively unimportant. In both cases I will be looking for characteristic and repeated figures, ways of telling and making sense of the lives of engineers that carry a specific freight of meaning. There are of course forms that are specific to biography, and equally there are forms that are specific to the novel. I hope that I have respected these. But these forms are themselves ways of articulating what are more fundamental shared ideological preoccupations. It is these more fundamental preoccupations which are my topic.

My contention, briefly, is this: that popular accounts of the lives of the engineers are enmeshed in magical notions of 'mechanical genius' and ideological notions of self-help — that is the debunking element in the essay — but that they also have very strong indications of a more socially and historically grounded account, especially in Smiles' biographies.

Notions of mechanical genius

Samuel Smiles' second volume of the *Lives of the Engineers* is especially rich in such notions. John Smeaton, we are told, like James Brindley, 'was impelled to the career on which he entered, by a like innate genius for construction'; John Rennie had 'an innate love of construction'; Joseph Huddart, the inventor of rope-making machinery, 'was attracted to the pursuit by the force of his genius, rather than by the peculiar direction of his education'.[1] As someone who has a singular lack of mechanical genius, I am not about to mock the claims for those who have it. However, reading these biographies, and the accounts of mechanical self-helpers in other sources, the story of their mechanical genius begins to take on the status of a conventional narrative unit or, in literary terms, a trope. The boy's genius (these are all stories about boys) invariably manifests itself in the construction of mechanical models, often showing dexterity and skill beyond those possessed by the local workmen. The fullest version of this trope comes in Smiles' biography of James Watt:

> Most of his spare time was thus devoted to mechanical adaptations of his own contrivance. A small forge was erected for him and a bench fitted up for his special use; and there he constructed many ingenious little objects, such as miniature cranes, pulleys, pumps and capstans. Out of a large silver coin he fabricated a punch-ladle, which is still preserved.[2]

That this is a widely shared trope can be seen from Charles Dickens' comic use of it in *Bleak House*, written some ten years before this passage. Dickens describes the upbringing of Rouncewell, the ironmaster — a figure to whom we shall return — in the following terms:

> . . . he took, when he was a schoolboy, to constructing steam-engines out of saucepans, and setting birds to draw their own water, with the least possible amount of labour; so assisting them with artful contrivance of hydraulic pressure, that a thirsty canary had only, in a literal sense, to put his shoulder to the wheel, and the job was done.[3]

Dickens' comic use of the trope here suggests at the very least a wide currency for it before Smiles' biographies were published.

Indeed, we find the trope appearing in a number of novels in the mid-nineteenth century, particularly novels which deal with men who have risen in life —

like the ironmaster in *Bleak House*. Thus we can find the trope in Geraldine Jewsbury's Manchester novel of 1851, *Marian Withers*; the heroine's father, John Withers, is a typical self-helping manufacturer, but he has got to his position by virtue of his inventive genius, which inspires him to the thought of a better design for a cotton-spinning machine. Similarly in another novel from the 1850s, Dinah Mariah Mulock's *John Halifax Gentleman*, the hero is also an orphan who makes his way in the world by his own efforts; in his childhood too, John Halifax demonstrates his mechanical genius. And finally in Edward Bulwer-Lytton's *'My Novel'*, published in 1854, which is predominantly a conservative narration of the self-helping story, there is nevertheless a character, Leonard Fairfield, who rises in life; Bulwer-Lytton makes him a poet, but there is a perfunctory allusion to the notion of mechanical genius in the presence of the widespread trope here too — Fairfield's mechanical genius leads him to patent a device for improving the steam engine.[4]

There is nothing inherently wrong with the idea that some children have more of a mechanical aptitude than others. Where it becomes a magical notion is when this aptitude is offered as itself a sufficient explanation for those children's later lives — in other words, when this aptitude is abstracted, by such notions as 'innate genius', from the full density of the social and cultural circumstances in which the aptitude can manifest itself and be developed. Smiles in particular is very good at suggesting these social and cultural circumstances, in ways which complement the more magical notions which are also to be found in his writings.

Notions of self-help

More serious, perhaps, is the ideological context in which the lives of the engineers are told. In the case of Samuel Smiles, we do not have to look far for this context, for he is of course most famous as the author of *Self-Help*, published in 1859. The notion of self-help is at the heart of a nexus of ideas and attitudes which together constitute a powerful ideological position. It is the moral counterpart to economic theories of laissez-faire, stressing the virtues of self-reliance, temperance and perseverance, which Smiles sought to sum up in the notion of 'character'.[5] *Self-Help* provides powerful narrative models — of a career, ultimately of a life — which can be used to explain one's own life and offered as models to aspirants. It has strongly anti-paternalist (in the mid-nineteenth century, anti-aristocratic) connotations, stressing as it does individual and self-sustained notions of worth. But it cuts the other way as well, seeking to detach the self-helping individual from the cultural and social connections which surround him, and implicitly to blame the vast majority of people who do not rise in life for their own failure. It is that aspect of notions of self-help which Charles Dickens satirised in *Hard Times*, singling this out as one of the 'fictions' of Coketown:

> Any capitalist there, who had made sixty thousand pounds out of sixpence, always professed to wonder why the sixty thousand nearest Hands didn't each make sixty thousand pounds out of sixpence, and more or less reproached them every one for not accomplishing the little feat. What I did you can do. Why don't you go and do it?[6]

However, Dickens' attitude to self-help is very much more complicated than this single quotation might suggest; for broadly speaking he is sympathetic to the idea, merely attacking overweening claims made for it.

Smiles developed the notion of self-help most fully in the book of that name, but he first elaborated the story of the self-helping individual to its fullest extent in *The Life of George Stephenson, Railway Engineer*, written in 1856 some three years before *Self-Help* itself. As far as Smiles developed ideas of self-help and the self-made man, he did so in a way that was completely imbricated in the history of engineering. On the other hand, it is important to recognise that Smiles was not the only person to tell stories of self-help — many other conduct or inspirational books of a similar kind were written in the 1850s and before, and the story of the individual who rises in life in its nineteenth-century versions is evidently a close descendant of the story of the industrious apprentice.[7] Smiles' manner of narrating the lives of the engineers in the later volumes of engineering lives makes the ideological 'capture' of these stories especially transparent. In effect he draws a moral from these lives in summarising chapters at the conclusion of each life, which provide a brief character portrait. In addition, Smiles' introduction to the *Lives of the Engineers* provides the moral context in which Smiles wishes their lives to be seen: 'These men gathered their practical knowledge in the workshop, or acquired it in manual labour. They rose to celebrity, mostly by their habits of observation, their powers of discrimination, their constant self-improvement, and their patient industry'.[8] This is a theme that is constantly repeated throughout Smiles' text — that engineers represent the national character in their 'perseverance in all undertakings' and their 'constancy of character'.[9] Still in the introduction, Smiles writes that:

> These men were strong-minded, resolute and ingenious, and were impelled to their special pursuits by the force of their constructive instincts. In most cases they had to make for themselves a way; for there were none to point out the road, which, until they entered upon their undertakings, had for the most part been untravelled. To our mind, there is almost a dramatic interest in their noble efforts, their defeats, their triumphs; and their constant rise, in spite of manifold obstructions and difficulties, from obscurity to fame.[10]

The ideological direction of this is plain enough, and I have said enough already on the notion of mechanical genius which underlies this account of engineers 'impelled to their special pursuits by the force of their constructive instincts'. There is a special interest, also, in the emphasis that Smiles seeks to give to these lives. I think there may be some slight defensiveness about that last sentence — 'To our mind, there is almost . . .' — which indicates a desire to substitute a different notion of dramatic interest and of defeats and triumphs to that which was prevalent at the time of Smiles' writing: perhaps a more pacific notion (we may note, for example, that Smiles describes the Duke of Bridgewater and James Brindley as 'heroes of industry and of *peace*'[11] [my emphasis]).

The list of virtues displayed by Smiles' heroes eventually becomes rather predictable. Of Hugh Myddleton, the surveyor of the New River that supplied London with drinking water in the early seventeenth century, he writes: 'Myddleton's success in life seems to have been attributable not less to his quick intelligence than to his laborious application and indomitable perseverance'; James Watt's 'greatest achievements were accomplished by unremitting application and industry'; John Smeaton 'was, throughout his whole career, a most industrious man — indeed, industry was the necessity and habit of his life'; and John Rennie 'thought little of fame, but a great deal of character and duty'.[12] Smiles had insisted on these same self-helping virtues in his earlier biography of George Stephenson, drawing the principal moral from it, in words attributed to Stephenson himself, 'Do as I have done — PERSEVERE!'.[13] In other words, in seeking to make more general sense of the various life-stories that he tells, Smiles repeatedly transforms these various and disparate people, drawn from quite different periods and cultures, into exemplars of the self-helping virtues, so that their lives are arranged to demonstrate the same self-helping message.

Notions of class

This way of thinking about engineers involves what can be described as an element of petty-bourgeois class pride. The opening sentences of the biography of James Watt state this theme ringingly:

> James Watt was born at Greenock, on the Clyde, on the 19th of January, 1736. His parents were of the middle class, industrious, intelligent, and religious people, with a character for probity which had descended to them from their 'forbears', and was cherished as their proudest inheritance. James Watt was thus emphatically well-born.[14]

This is the writing of someone proud and ready to declare a distinctive class notion of value, implicitly mobilised against more aristocratic notions of good breeding. In fact, Smiles further insists that the origins of many of the engineers were 'humble', and is happy to emphasise, for example, that they retained dialect speech in many cases throughout their lives. However, this is by no means an egalitarian attitude; another of the persistent tropes of Smiles' biographies is the distance that the self-helping engineer has to set between himself and the habits and levels of skill of the workmen with whom he comes into contact. Hence the insistence on these engineers' temperance, their efforts to overcome such customs as Saint Monday (i.e. the custom of spending Monday and sometimes Tuesday drinking rather than working), and their distinctive and often heroic commitment to their work — the biographies are full of anecdotes of engineers walking vast distances to particular jobs, or working all night to get a particular task finished before a deadline.

Characterisation in the nineteenth-century novel

Samuel Smiles attached particular meanings to the engineers' lives that he narrated. They are told as part of an ideology of self-help, promoting the distinctively petty-bourgeois virtues, and narrated with a strong element of class pride. This is not a position that is distinctive to Smiles. We can see it strongly retold in the characterisation of the ironmaster in *Bleak House,* who shows a comically indicated mechanical genius and who similarly displays all the self-helping virtues. Charles Dickens returns to a similar figure in *Little Dorrit,* published 1855–1857, where the character of Daniel Doyce is a classic Smilesian self-helping engineer, an inventor whose great discovery is balked by the officialdom of the Circumlocution Office. This is how Doyce is described:

> . . . he was the son of a north-country blacksmith, and had originally been apprenticed by his widowed mother to a lock-maker; that he had 'struck out a few little things' at the lock-maker's, which had led to his being released from his indentures with a present, which present had enabled him to gratify his ardent wish to bind himself to a working engineer, under whom he had laboured hard, learned hard and lived hard, seven years.[15]

Both this characterisation, and that of the ironmaster in *Bleak House,* strike me as wholly positive; they are in fact Smilesian heroes of self-help, and in the same way as Smiles, Dickens narrates their stories to emphasise their distinctive worth when contrasted with the aristocrat-dominated institutions with which they come into contact. Thus Doyce is pitted against the Circumlocution Office, who refuse to provide state aid to develop his invention (what it is, is unclear, but one theory asserts that Dickens based the character of Doyce on Charles Babbage); similarly, the ironmaster is confronted by Lord Dedlock, shown as the epitome of aristocratic ignorance and reaction. In this, Dickens demonstrates an element of middle-class radicalism, repeating some of the themes common to such radicalism in the mid-century — that the state was dominated by place-hunting aristocrats inimical to the spirit of enterprise.[16]

In fact, the inextricability of the lives of engineers from questions of self-help and thus questions of class is one of the striking aspects of the way that the lives of engineers appear in the nineteenth-century novel — which is, to tell the truth, not very much. Indeed, the characters of the ironmaster and Doyce are the most prominent characterisations that I know of in the corpus of the nineteenth-century novel. Generally, as in the indications of 'mechanical genius', engineering skills are little more than conventional explanations of a rise in life, while the real interest in a novel is to be found in more domestic questions — above all, in how the self-made individual and his family will negotiate relations with more traditional areas of social and cultural worth or prestige. Perhaps it is not very surprising that the aesthetics of the novel should not stretch to the triumphs of civil engineering, though we have seen that Smiles certainly thought that his engineering lives had a 'dramatic interest', and Carlyle also proposed that the national epic should no longer be 'arms and the man' but 'tools and the man'.

Social and cultural contexts

I began by asserting that this essay would not be an exercise in debunking, though so far readers would be forgiven for assuming that that is indeed what they had been reading. But Smiles also offers the suggestions of a much more satisfying account of the lives of the engineers than the ideological capture of these stories by self-help would suggest; that is to say an account which situates and begins to explain these diverse lives in the very specific social and cultural circumstances in which they were lived. This is definitely not achieved in the introduction, though even here it seems to me to be trembling on the brink of a fully historical account:

> [England] fought wonderfully, and boasted of many victories; but she was gradually becoming less powerful as a State, until about the middle of the last century, when a number of ingenious and inventive men, without apparent relation to each other, arose in various parts of the kingdom, and succeeded in giving an immense impulse to all the branches of the national industry; the result of which has been a harvest of wealth and prosperity, perhaps without a parallel in the history of the world.[17]

To notice a passage such as this is perhaps no more than to observe that Smiles was writing before the notion of the industrial revolution had become widely established.[18] The point is that elsewhere Smiles does move beyond the notion of 'ingenious and inventive men' to place them securely in the particular cultural and economic context in which their ingenuity and inventiveness could be fully exploited.

One of the fullest and most satisfying accounts to do this is concerned with the early life of John Rennie, the great bridge and dock engineer. He grew up on a small farm in the east Lothians, and for a time worked as an assistant to a local millwright, Andrew Meikle. Smiles' account duly alludes to Rennie's 'innate love of instruction', but also goes to some pains to locate Meikle's own contrivances and improvements in agricultural machinery in the particular changes in lowland agriculture which gave them their immediate impetus. Thus Smiles paints a vivid picture of the state of Scottish agriculture in the early part of the eighteenth century, and draws attention to the specific social and economic forces which later transformed it. We learn of the introduction of long rents, the capital invested in improved farm buildings and machinery, and the introduction of enclosures, and indeed of the method of banking which financed these changes. All this provides the essential context in which the improvements of a man like Meikle become comprehensible, and which go some way to explain how the admitted mechanical aptitude of someone like Rennie can come to seem significant and exploitable.

Equally, in one of the fullest biographies, that of James Watt and Matthew Boulton, Smiles is always careful to locate Watt's specifically engineering difficulties, as he encountered them in the effort to improve the steam engine, in the specific economic circumstances in which they were effected, so that the particular methods of payment for the engines were very closely related to efficiency gains — indeed, it is clear from Smiles' account that savings in fuel efficiency were the very raison d'être of Watt's improvement on Newcomen's engine. But there is a wider interest in this biography also in the account that Smiles provides of the cultural milieu of Boulton in the West Midlands in the latter half of the eighteenth century. Smiles gives a full account of the Lunar Society, that network of progressive middle-class intellectuals and manufacturers who managed to combine enlightened interest in, and patronage of, science and the arts, with investment in and running some of the largest manufacturing enterprises. It becomes very clear from this volume of *The Lives of the Engineers* how Boulton's interest in Watt's experiments, and indeed how Watt's own persistence in them, emerge from a coherent and carefully described social, economic and cultural milieu. We are a long way here from the 'apparently isolated men in the middle of the eighteenth century' that appear in Smiles' introduction. As a general principle, it seems at least likely that the engineering achievements of one generation will draw upon those of a preceding generation; in this context it is relevant to recall Robert Stephenson's belief that a mining engineer received the most suitable training for a railway engineer, an opinion quoted by Victoria Haworth elsewhere in this volume.[19]

These are by no means isolated examples in Smiles' writings; quite the contrary, in fact, for he characteristically works by describing the social context from which the engineers emerge, even if this at times seems like little more than local colour and can coexist with some of the more magical explanations to which I have alluded. Thus Smiles provides a vivid picture of Watt's native Greenock in the mid-eighteenth century, and of Manchester before the building of the Bridgewater canal, and of Brindley's native Derbyshire. Perhaps the fullest such account that he gives occurs in the volume on the road-builders John Metcalf and Thomas Telford, where a substantial portion of the volume is devoted to describing the state of Britain in the seventeenth and eighteenth centuries before the building of a good road system. This is in effect indistinguishable from social history, in which the interconnectedness of transport systems, trade and what Smiles calls 'civilisation', is vividly established.

I find that I have now reverted to the use of scare quotes again, as a way of suggesting that this social-historical theme in Smiles' writing is not without its own problems. These are of course that engineering becomes, in this account, part of the history of 'progress', that insidious but not wholly false idea in which history appears as a march which proceeds onwards and upwards from darkness to light. Thus in the section of *Lives of the Engineers* called 'Early roads and modes of travelling', Smiles concludes the chapter on Scotland with these words:

> . . . and Scotland continued to lie in ruins almost till our own day, when it has again been rescued from barrenness, more effectually even than before, by the combined influences of roads, education, and industry.[20]

'The combined influences of roads, education, and industry' — it is a peculiarly evocative phrase, in which lurk both a genuinely social-historical understanding of the material infrastructure which underlies any culture, and an offensive smugness and complacency both about the culture of 'industry' and the supposed ignorance and barbarity which precedes it.

However, this is not the final note that I wish to strike with respect to Smiles, whose writing can certainly exhibit complacency, who is keen to load the lives of his engineers with directly moralistic and ideological meanings, and who perpetuated some myths about Stephenson and Brindley. He also saw more than all this, and was capable of wider sympathies. In particular, his writing can be seen as contributing to the history of civil society, seeking to explain the evident and spectacular changes in British social life from the late eighteenth century onwards in terms that pay due attention to the myriad social and economic circumstances that produced those changes.

It needs to be emphasised that I am by no means describing a sequential progression in Smiles' writing, in which he passes from one inadequate conception of engineering history to another, more satisfactory one. On the contrary, it seems to me that both conceptions are similarly present in his writing, and indeed I have probably over-stressed the potentially social-historical account in order to counter too restrictive a view of Smiles as the simple ideologue of self-help. Nevertheless, the potential for such a reading of Smiles certainly seems to me to be present, as a not fully developed possibility that runs against the general ideological current of his work.

Thomas Carlyle and the notion of heroism

A minor element in Samuel Smiles' writing is that rather uncertain attempt to offer his engineers as providing a heroic, but distinctively pacific and commercial, alternative history. The nineteenth-century writer who contrasts most interestingly with Smiles in this respect is Thomas Carlyle, who very consciously sought to provide a heroic account of history, but who also sought to extend the notion of the heroic to include engineers such as James Brindley and Richard Arkwright. But if Smiles sought to make his engineers into exemplars of self-help and the pioneers of progress and improvement, for Carlyle they were heroes of another kind, battling against nature and their fellows in a desperate existential struggle whose rewards were no less than the transformation of the world. This is how Carlyle, in the essay 'Chartism', describes the struggles of Arkwright to produce the water-frame:

> Richard Arkwright, it would seem, was not a beautiful man; no romance-hero with haughty eyes, Apollo-lip, and gesture like the herald Mercury; a plain almost gross, bag-cheeked, almost pot-bellied Lancashire man, with an air of painful reflection, yet also of copious free digestion; a man stationed by the community to shave certain dusty beards, in the Northern parts of England, at a halfpenny each. To such end, we say, by forethought, oversight, accident and arrangement, had Richard Arkwright been, by the community of England and his own consent, set apart. Nevertheless, in strapping of razors, in lathering of dusty beards, and the contradictions and confusions attendant thereon, the man had notions in that rough head of his; spindles, shuttles, wheels and contrivances plying ideally within the same: rather hopeless-looking; which, however, he did at last bring to bear. Not without difficulty! His townsfolk rose in mob round him, for threatening to shorten labour, to shorten wages; so that he had to fly, with broken wash-pots, scattered household, and seek refuge elsewhere. Nay his wife too, as I learn, rebelled; burnt his wooden model of his spinning-wheel; resolute that he should stick to his razors rather; for which, however, he decisively, as thou wilt rejoice to understand, packed her out of doors. O reader, what a Historical Phenomenon is that bag-cheeked, potbellied, much-enduring, much inventing barber! French Revolutions were a-brewing to resist the same in any measure, imperial Kaisers were impotent without the cotton and cloth of England; and it was this man that had to give England the power of cotton.[21]

Here, as can be seen, the stakes are rather higher than in Smiles' altogether more modest prose, though we can see some of the same themes that are to be found in Smiles. First, there is a notion of mechanical genius present in this passage, although it is given a rather grander description than Smiles habitually gives it. Then there is the same effort, perhaps only implicit in Smiles, to substitute a new conception of the heroic for an outmoded and conventional one, as when Carlyle in the above passage insists upon Arkwright's unprepossessing physical features, so unlike the presumed physical characteristics of the conventional hero. And there is the similar trope of the hostility of the local working population to the technical improvements of the heroic figure. But in Carlyle's prose the hero is unmistakably pitched in a remarkable individual battle to wrest his invention from the ideal world, and in this prose also the consequences are explicitly seen in heroic and world-historical terms; this is no longer a sober account of the gradual onward progress of civilisation, but an account of an invention that will have a direct effect on the destiny of nations.

Similar themes are expounded at fuller length in *Past and Present*, published in 1843. Here James

Brindley figures in a similar way to Arkwright in 'Chartism':

> The rugged Brindley has little to say for himself; the rugged Brindley, when difficulties accumulate on him, retires silent, 'generally to his bed;' retires 'sometimes for three days together to his bed, that he may be in perfect privacy there,' and ascertain in his rough head how the difficulties may be overcome. The ineloquent Brindley, behold he *has* chained seas together; his ships do visibly float over valleys, invisibly through the hearts of mountains; the Mersey and the Thames, the Humber and the Severn have shaken hands: Nature most audibly answers, Yea![22]

Once again, Carlyle insists upon the unattractiveness of Brindley, his *ruggedness*; in this quotation it can be more clearly seen how Brindley is engaged in an existential struggle with nature, the outcome of which is the triumphant ships floating over valleys and through mountains. The immediate context for this quotation is an argument in which Carlyle contrasts to his advantage the man of practice such as Brindley to the man of theory; later in *Past and Present* Carlyle wishes to draw yet another implication from the lives of British engineers. I have already quoted his fine phrase that the national epic has now become 'tools and the man' (in implicit contrast with the beginning of the *Aeneid*, 'I sing of arms and the man'). It is of course significant that this is to be a national epic; when Carlyle tries for his grandest and most heroic prose, he reaches not for the language of classical myth but for that of the Northern gods and heroes, with whom the heroic deeds of contemporary engineers — in 'shivering mountains asunder' and in taming the oceans — are to be directly associated. There is finally for Carlyle a direct racial connection between Odin and Thor, and Arkwright, Brindley and James Watt.

Conclusion

The bringing out of ideological meanings which were invested in the lives of engineers in nineteenth-century writing potentially leads us in diverse and perhaps unexpected directions. The theme of self-help might be supplemented by considering the iconography of labour; famous nineteenth-century paintings like Ford Madox-Brown's *Work* or Henrietta Ward's *Palissy the Potter* are both relevant here. But I have attempted to restrict my topic to the representations of engineering proper, which, though they were inextricably entangled with notions of self-help, could not explain engineering success simply in terms of perseverance. I favour social and historical explanations of the extraordinary achievements in engineering that mark what we now call the Industrial Revolution, and these are just the kind of explanations that go against the grain of typical nineteenth-century accounts — whether these accounts are cast in the more modest mode of self-help or in the full-blown heroic mode of Carlyle. Yet another, more sympathetic, emphasis can be found in the writing of Smiles; an emphasis on the social and historical location of those acts of engineering, in the light of which they become more comprehensible but not one whit less remarkable.

Notes and references

1 Smiles, S, *Lives of the Engineers*, II, 'Harbours, VIII, lighthouses, bridges, Smeaton and Rennie' (London: John Murray, 1891), pp85, 194, 361. *Lives of the Engineers* was first published in 1861–1862. Because editions vary in the way that the material is distributed between volumes, the contents of the volumes in the edition used here is listed: I, 'Early engineering, Vermuyden, Myddelton, Perry, James Brindley' (1874); II, 'Harbours, lighthouses, bridges, Smeaton and Rennie' (1891); III, 'History of roads, Metcalfe, Telford' (1874); IV, 'Boulton and Watt' (n.d.).

2 Smiles, S, *Lives of the Engineers*, IV, p15

3 Dickens, C, *Bleak House* (London: Penguin, 1971), pp134–35. *Bleak House* was first published in 1851–1852.

4 Geraldine Jewsbury, *Marian Withers* (1851); Dinah Maria Mulock [Mrs Craik], *John Halifax, Gentleman* (1856); Edward Bulwer-Lytton, *'My Novel', by Pisistratus Caxton; or, Varieties in English Life* (1854)

5 For the notion that the ideal of self-help is 'the moral concomitant of the economic principle of laissez-faire', see Kovacevic, I, *Fact into Fiction* (Leicester: Leicester University Press, 1975), p35.

6 Dickens, C, *Hard Times* (London: Penguin,

1969), p152. *Hard Times* was originally published in 1854.

7 Mention may be made here of two such conduct books from the 1850s that predate Smiles, both anonymous: *Men Who have Risen* (n.d., but published in the 1850s from internal evidence); *Success in Life; A Book for Young Men* (1852).

8 Smiles, S, *Lives of the Engineers*, I, pxvii

9 Smiles, S, *Lives of the Engineers*, I, pxxi

10 Smiles, S, *Lives of the Engineers*, I, pxxii

11 Smiles, S, *Lives of the Engineers*, I, p240

12 Smiles, S, *Lives of the Engineers*, I, p67; IV, p406; II, pp177, 378

13 Smiles, S, *The Life of George Stephenson: Railway Engineer*, 2nd edn (London: Murray, 1858), p496

14 Smiles, S, *Lives of the Engineers*, IV, p3

15 Dickens, C, *Little Dorrit* (London: Penguin, 1967), pp232–33

16 At the time of writing *Little Dorrit*, Dickens was a member of the Administrative Reform Association, a typical organ of middle-class radicalism.

17 Smiles, S, *Lives of the Engineers*, I, pxvii

18 Toynbee's *Industrial Revolution*, 1884, first gave the term wide currency.

19 See p47

20 Smiles, S, *Lives of the Engineers*, III, p59

21 Carlyle, T, 'Chartism', in *English and Other Miscellanies* (London: Everyman's Library, n.d.), pp219–20. This was first published 1839.

22 Carlyle, T, *Past and Present* (London: Everyman's Library, 1978), p153

Plate 1. James Watt by Henry Raeburn dated 1815, and in the Henry E Huntington Library and Art Gallery, California, USA.

A

TREATISE

OF

MECHANICS,

THEORETICAL, PRACTICAL,

AND

DESCRIPTIVE.

BY

OLINTHUS GREGORY, A. M.

OF THE ROYAL MILITARY ACADEMY, WOOLWICH.

SECOND EDITION, WITH IMPROVEMENTS.

VOL. II.

CONTAINING

Remarks on the Nature, Construction, and Simplification of Machinery, on Friction, Rigidity of Cords, First Movers, &c.

AND

Descriptions of many curious and useful Machines.

——Talem intelligo Philosophiam naturalem, quæ non abeat in fumos speculationum subtilium, aut sublimium; sed que efficaciter operetut, ad sublevandi vitæ humanæ incommoda. BACON. *De Aug. Sci.*

LONDON:

PRINTED FOR GEORGE KEARSLEY, FLEET-STREET.

1807.

Plate 2. Title page of Olinthus Gregory's *Treatise of Mechanics*, 2 (1807), in which Jabez Carter Hornblower's later-suppressed account of the history of the steam engines was published.

Plate 3. Wherry Mine in work circa 1794 with the Hornblower engine house shown on the left (from Hawkins, J, 'On submarine mines', *Transactions of the Royal Geological Society of Cornwall,* 1 (1818), frontispiece).

Plate 4. William Mackenzie (1845) from the painting by T H Illidge, engraved by G R Ward.

77

Day Book 5th June 1835 —

Warrington Contract Dr

(48) To 2 time Cheque Books c — - 6 -

Yarrow Contract Dr

(49) To 1 order Book - 7 -
2 Time Cheque Books - 6 -
- 13 -

John Chadwick Cr

(36) By Lime 45 Cwts c 1/- 2 5 -

Yarrow Contract Dr

To 357 Rails (square) 12.15.3.0 @ 7/- 89 10 3
1 force pump bottom 2 - -
2, 4 Inch pipes for do - 14 -
1 lever do - 6 -
34 Axles for Small Waggons 2/- 3 8 -
65 Wheels for do 1/6 4 17 6
70 Wrot Iron Loops for do 6 1 15 -
2 Washer Axles, to make large hammers 1 8 -
2 Anvils 4 - -
1 Vice - 10 -
(49) 43 Battens
7. 3 Inch planks 1/- 6 9 -
1 long Broad plank 1 1 -
70 Wrot Iron Axles for large Waggons - 8 -
510 Temporary Wooden Sleepers 6 40 16 8
31 large Cast Iron steps for large Waggons 12 10 -
1 pair 26 Inch Bellowses 3/- 4 13 -
1 pair 34 Inch do 4 - -
1 Centre [illegible] do 5 10 -

Day Book 6th June 1835

Yarrow Contract Brot over 193 18 1
2 large Wheels & Axles Complete (large Wagr.) 4 - -
16 points & Crossings for temporary railroad 1 4 -
10 Wheels for large Waggons 17 2 -
11 Stays for Small Wheels - 4 -
p Boat Mary Thos Driver Captain, and
p Boat Jane of Burnley, Captn Kershaw
(49) Mr Davis 3 Journeys 3 days oiling c 1/8 - 5 -
9 610 Temporary Sleepers 6 15 5 -
40 3 Inch planks 6 - -
7 points for Small rail road - 10 6
1 Switch - 7 -
p Boat Jane of Burnley — 238 15 7

Warrington Contract

256 Temporary Sleepers c 6 6 8 -
6 Lay Baulks 6 - -
10 large Waggons 160/- 80 - -
(48) 2 Stone Lewises 2 - -
9 Wheelbarrows 15/- 6 15 -
3 fire grates 5/- - 15 -
5 days for men load Materials c 2/8 - 13 4
Mr Davis 3 Journeys oiling 1/8 - 5 -
102 16 4

Yarrow Contract Dr

(49) To 8½ days Men load Materials c 2/8 1 2 8

L & Manchester Railway Co Dr

To 5½ day Cattle [illegible] 0 19 3
[illegible] c 5/- 5 10 -

Plate 5. William Mackenzie's Day Book, 1835, showing entries for Warrington (GJR), Yarrow (NUR) and Liverpool and Manchester Railway contracts being carried out concurrently.

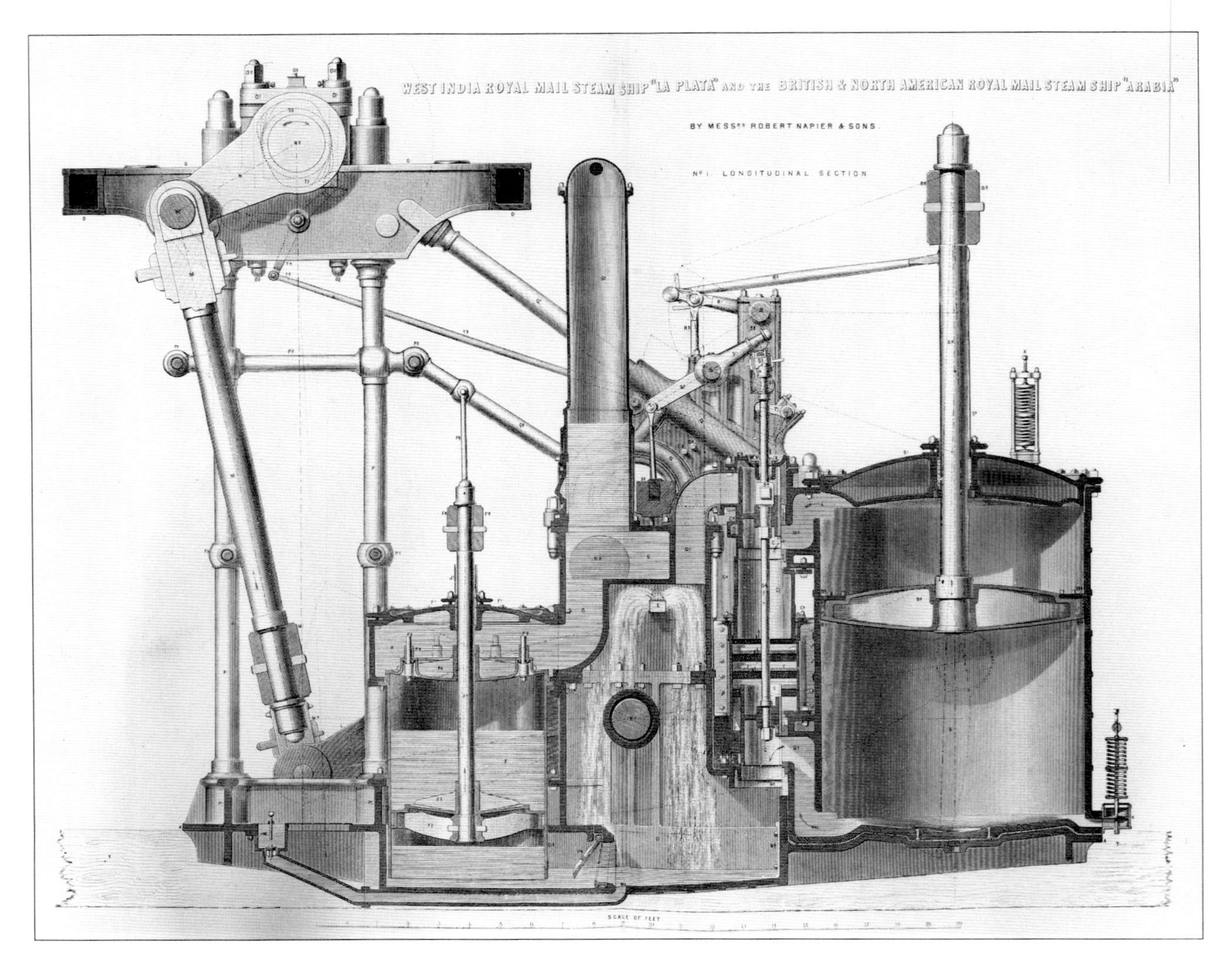

Plate 6. Longitudinal section of the engines of *Arabia* and *La Plata*, 1852, showing David Elder's design of slide valve, the separate grid-iron expansion valve, extended working barrel of the air pump and the hot well with closed top (Macquorn Rankine, W J (ed), *Shipbuilding Theoretical and Practical* (Glasgow: W Mackenzie, 1866), plate N/1).

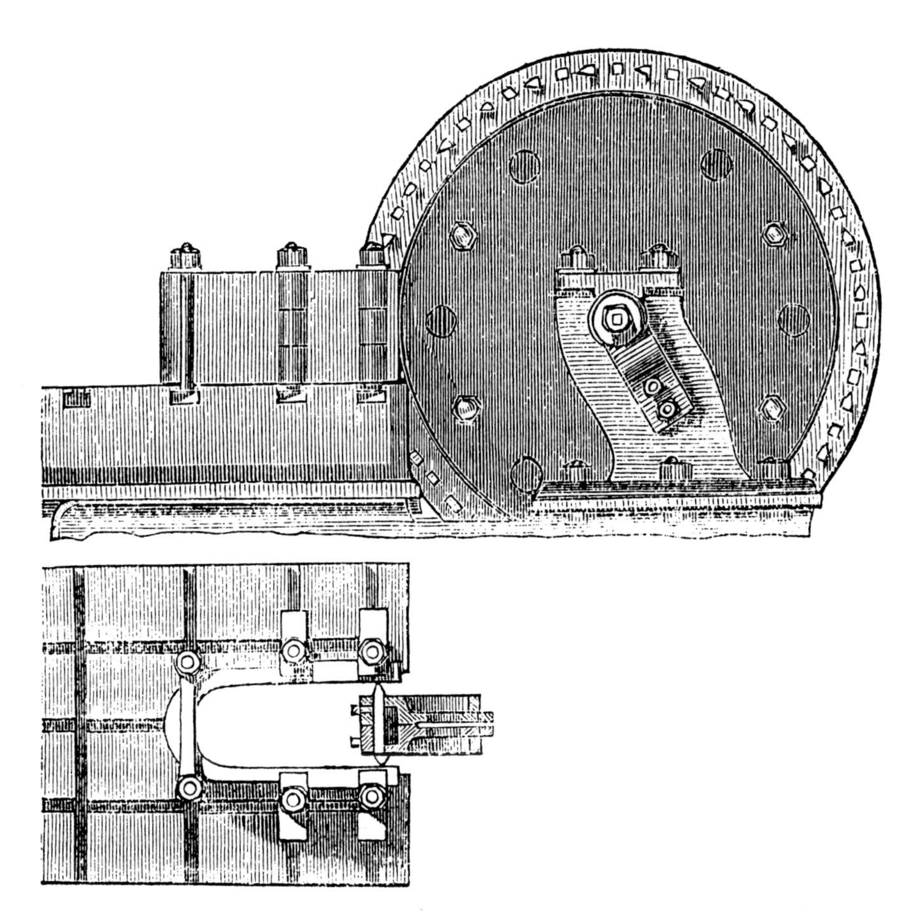

Plate 7. 'Paring machine' for finishing the straps of connecting rods and side rods, 1833 (*The Engineer*, 21 (1866), p256).

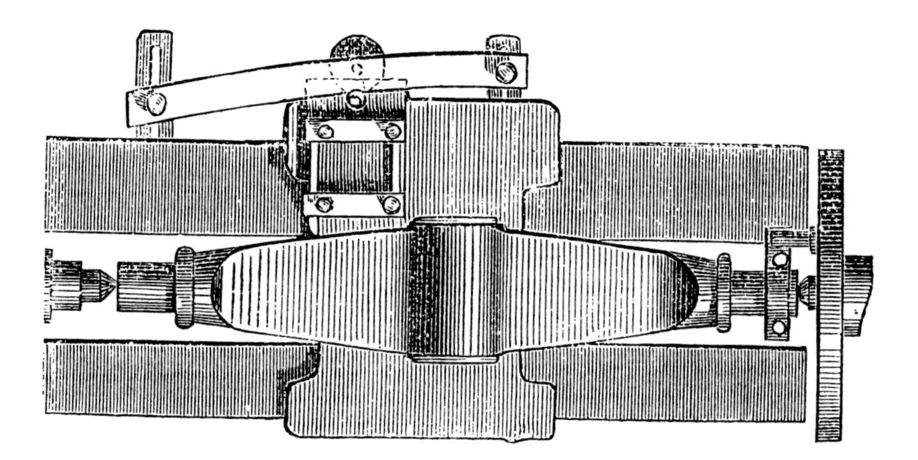

Plate 8. Lathe copying device for forming the fish-belly shape of crossheads and rods (*The Engineer*, 21 (1866), p256).

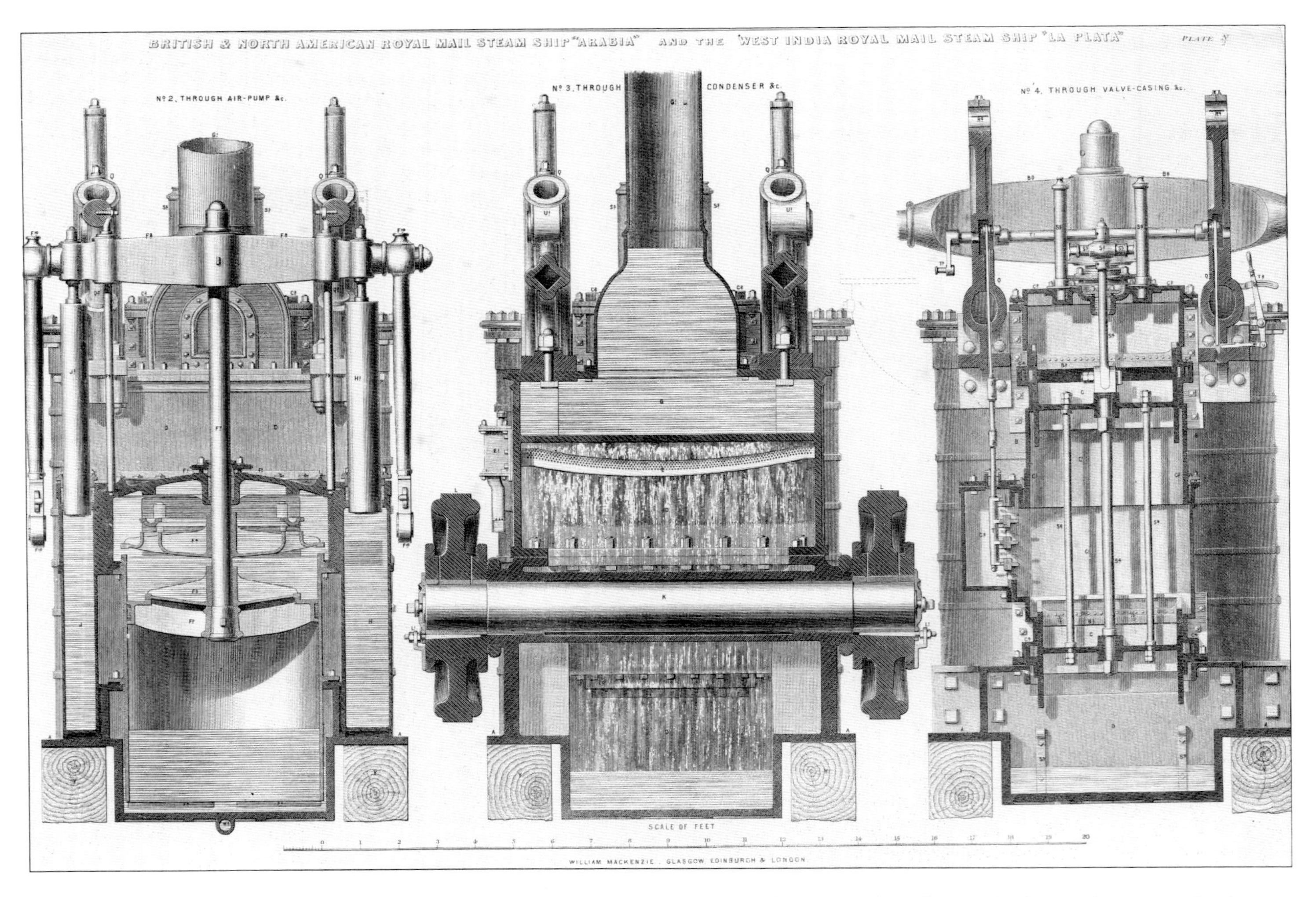

Plate 9. Transverse sections of the engines of *Arabia* and *La Plata*. The middle view shows the tube cast in the condenser to take the main centre. In the right-hand section the grid-iron expansion valve is clearly visible (Macquorn Rankine, W J (ed), *Shipbuilding Theoretical and Practical* (Glasgow: W Mackenzie, 1866), plate N/2).

Inspiration and instigation: four great railway engineers

Victoria Haworth

John Rastrick (1780–1856), John Stephenson (1794–1848), Robert Stephenson (1803–1859) and Joseph Locke (1805–1860), were recognised by their contemporaries as being pre-eminent within their profession. On the death of Locke, *The Times* stated that with Robert Stephenson and I K Brunel, Locke 'may be said to have completed the Triumvirate of the engineering world'.[1]

While Brunel's reputation has remained on an illustrious pedestal, Locke and Stephenson have fallen from grace, particularly during the last two decades. Whereas Brunel was a general engineer turning his hand to road bridges, steam ships and railways, concentrating his efforts in the south-west corner of England, Stephenson and Locke were nationally and internationally renowned railway engineers. A scholarly approach to early railway history has often been sadly lacking. The railway enthusiast is probably aware that they rank as the most prolific railway engineers ever, constructing over 4000 miles of railway network between them in Great Britain alone. Robert Stephenson also introduced railway networks to Belgium, the German and Italian states, Norway and Switzerland; Joseph Locke to France, Spain and Holland.[2] But there has been a tendency to consider the two railway chiefs in mediocre terms, as ineffectual figureheads with their associates and employees taking initiative as part of collaborative teamwork, even though contemporary evidence shows that this was not the case.

Parliamentary Committees. Robert Stephenson and Joseph Locke

During the inquiry into the use of iron in railway structures held between November 1847 and April 1848, the leading railway engineers listed their major achievements. Joseph Locke stated:

> I was the resident engineer on the Liverpool and Manchester railway during its construction from 1826 to 1830 . . . I afterwards constructed the Grand Junction or Liverpool and Birmingham line, the South Western line, the Sheffield and Manchester line, the Lancaster and Preston line, the Lancaster and Carlisle line, the Caledonian and Scottish Central, the Scottish Midland, and the Glasgow, Paisley and Greenock and various others.

When asked by cross-examining counsel whether in all these cases he was employed as engineer-in-chief or if in some cases he acted as assistant engineer, Locke replied: 'I was engineer-in-chief to all the railways I constructed after the Liverpool and Manchester Railway.' Asked how long he had acted in the capacity of civil engineer, Locke was unambiguous: 'I was educated in it and have practised it all my life.'[3] A sweeping statement, but correct. His father and grandfather were mining engineers and the tuition he received at home was more relevant to his career than the four-year formal education at Barnsley Grammar School. By the age of eighteen, Locke had served a total of five years' apprenticeship as a mining engineer, first at Pelaw, County Durham, under William Stobart — one of the most 'eminent colliery viewers in the district'[4]—and then under his own father.

Robert Stephenson considered a mining engineer to receive the most suitable training to qualify as a railway engineer, being able to survey, sink shafts, construct railways, tunnels and stationary engines, manage men and ensure profitable returns.[5] It is therefore not surprising that a mining engineer, John Stephenson,[6] became the mainstay contractor of both Robert Stephenson and Locke. Throughout his independent career, Robert Stephenson chose another fully fledged mining engineer, Frank Forster,[7] to be his right-hand man. Stephenson himself had not been as fortunate as Locke. Denied the rudiments of education at home by his father's limited literacy, his formal schooling comprised four years at John Bruce's Academy,[8] Newcastle upon Tyne, ostensibly to begin an apprenticeship as a mining engineer under Nicholas Wood, the head viewer of Killingworth Collieries,[9] but in fact his father, George Stephenson, needed his services. In 1819, George Stephenson secured the contract for building a railway from Hetton Colliery to the staithes at Sunderland and, at the same time, was given the itinerant post of enginewright to all the Grand Allies pits in the area, necessitating his son's permanent presence at the Killingworth engine workshop.[10] The young mining engineer did not complete his training.[11] After two years his father needed his services again for the engineering work on the Stockton & Darlington Railway in the autumn of 1821 and 'Several gentlemen who came in contact with him during the survey of the line had been so struck with his natural force of intellect that they represented to his father the propriety and indeed the imperative duty of giving him a college education.'[12] Although sending his son to Cambridge was well within his means, George Stephenson did not wish 'to make his son a gentleman'.[13] However, he agreed to Edinburgh, where the academic year formed one session only, from late October to April, leaving the student free to find an occupation in the summer months. Most of a railway's construction was done during the long daylight hours of the summer months. Before becoming an undergraduate in 1822, Robert Stephenson had organised the construction of sections already authorised under the first Stockton & Darlington Railway Acts.[14] He drew up the contracts in March and April 1822.[15] Contractors would then report to him at the Killingworth engine workshop where he was still based in spite of the termination of his employment at the Colliery as under viewer,[16] while his father looked and played the part on the line. In a crisis Robert was called for and he would spend time working on site.[17] Work proceeded rapidly and the first rails were laid on 18 May 1822. During the winter of 1822–1823, Robert Stephenson undoubtedly enjoyed the stimulation of a university education. However, his father procrastinated concerning going to London for the second Stockton & Darlington Railway Act.[18] In order to accompany his father and facilitate the Bill, Robert Stephenson left Edinburgh after five months, destined not to return as a student. His full-time services were needed as managing director of the world's first purpose-built locomotive factory.[19]

Throughout his career, Robert Stephenson gave evidence before Parliamentary Select Committees, often stating his early engineering experience. During the proceedings of the Newcastle & Carlisle Railway Bill in March 1829 he testified that his railway construction and works experience had begun in 1819, but with regard to steam-engine building '. . . I have attended to machinery all of my life'.[20] This again was not such an exaggerated statement as it may appear. Richard Trevithick sat young Robert on his knee 'many a night'[21] and the inventor was known to have taken working models of his high-pressure engine with him on his promotion tours. A contemporary witness claimed that it was because of Trevithick's influence that Stephenson 'became an engineer'.[22] Also Robert sat night after night with his father, a brakesman at Willington Quay and then at Killingworth in 1805 until 1812 when he became an enginewright, discussing maintenance problems on stationary steam engines, parts of the machinery being brought into the house: '. . . to help father was the proudest work which the boy then, and ever after could take part in. When the little engine was set up at Ochre Colliery to pump it dry, Robert was scarcely absent for an hour.'[23]

Cross-examining counsel placed Robert under severe scrutiny. When asked if a mechanical training entitled him to assume the label of railway engineer, Robert answered in the affirmative; experience alone was sufficient. Uncharacteristically he boasted: 'I think I could make an ordinary man understand levelling in a day,' and added, 'I think it is quite essential that a civil engineer should understand machinery.'[24]

At the 1847–1848 Royal Commission Inquiry Robert Stephenson confirmed:

> The London & Birmingham was the first great work which I had to execute, afterwards the continuous lines of railway up to Berwick, including the North Midland, Birmingham to Derby, the York and North Midland, the Newcastle and Darlington and the Berwick and Newcastle.

On being asked to verify whether he acted as the chief engineer, Robert answered: 'Always as engineer-in-chief.'[25] Clarification was also sought concerning the two Stephensons' names on the prospectuses of all these railways. Robert acted as sole engineer-in-chief, doing the engineering work expected of the appointment: directing the survey, designing structures under and over the railway, writing reports, organising the construction and supervising the works to a successful conclusion. Concerning the London & Birmingham Railway, he wrote in his 1834 diary:

11 February At Kilburn Office writing specifications and sketching bridges.

19 April At Weedon gave further instructions to Mr Forster.

15 May At St John's Wood all day writing letter and designing Bridges for Birmingham end.
20 June At Meeting of Board. At Birmingham for the purpose of explaining contract and specifications.
15 August At Kilsby — gave Forster instructions to proceed with the survey.
30 September At St John's Wood . . . calculating Kilsby Tunnel . . . calculating the Wolverton Viaduct.
5 December Wolverton Viaduct . . . considered the abutment too weak.
31 December At St John's Wood writing letter, examining plans & contracts — Stone blocks let to Forest of Dean People — They evidently don't understand the contract. It is imperative for them to comply with the stipulations.[26]

While working on the Birmingham & Derby Junction, the North Midland and the Sheffield & Rotherham, Robert Stephenson wrote in his 1839 diary:

16 July At Derby about the railway station of that town.
18 July At Sheffield and over the Sheffield & Rotherham Works.
19 July At Tapton to negotiate the purchase of land for railway station.[27]

Not content with receiving recognition for doing the vital promotion work and ensuring full subscription lists, George Stephenson also insisted on the title of engineer-in-chief.[28] His was the essential name on a railway prospectus, as revealed during the proceedings prior to the London & Brighton Railway Act, when the elder Stephenson claimed credit for the detailing of survey work and then had to admit to not being involved with any engineering preliminaries at all.

Counsel: Your name was put to it as principal engineer and you signed the estimate . . . the father should not put his name upon the credit of the son unless he has done the work.
George Stephenson: I have brought him up since a child . . . and I ought to have some benefit.[29]

In his manuscript memoirs Locke claimed to be: 'The leading pioneer together with Robert Stephenson . . . in making the plans and specifications for the first railway in England[30]. . . and that their employer George Stephenson only ever offered "nominal leadership"[31]. . . on the Grand Junction Railway he was "an entirely Titular Chief".'[32] Evidence given before Parliamentary Select Committees, railway company minute books and contemporary letters confirm Locke's claim. Looking at the documents objectively, L T C Rolt came to the conclusion that 'detailed survey work' or 'systematic organisation' necessary for the construction of a new railway was beyond George Stephenson.[33] Under the auspices of 'George Stephenson & Son' the work-load fell to the joint chief engineer, Robert Stephenson, and the chief clerk, Locke, who was never apprenticed to his master.[34] The strain of responsibility for Locke, still a teenager when Robert Stephenson left for South America in June 1824, is most evident from his correspondence:

What a pity that Nature did not destine me for a Poet! . . . But alas I am unbless'd with such God like gifts, and must be content to bear that chain of existence allotted to me — since writing to you I have been busily engaged levelling and surveying a proposed line of Railway from Leeds to Hull a distance of 50 miles.[35]

Locke later gave evidence: ' . . . I set out the line. Mr Stephenson was busy in London; and I showed him the plan and he approved.'[36] George Stephenson's counter-signature was placed on railway plans and reports long after the event. A contemporary biographer of Locke's remarked: 'Difficulties were many, encouragements few . . .'; by being earnest and hopeful '. . . these were dispensed with and overcome'.[37]

In retrospect Locke wrote: 'The absence of Robert Stephenson cast more responsibility on me, but helped me all the more to acquire an early knowledge of the practical parts of my profession.'[38] To his friend in voluntary exile he gave an account of his activities:

Since finishing that line (Leeds to Hull) I have been levelling one between Manchester & Bolton for which we are going to Parliament next Sessions and I trust the levels will be found to be correct — No doubt but you would hear of the Manchester & Liverpool Levels which has affected the interest of your Father very much, we must endeavour by our future attention to regain that opinion which we have late lost.[39]

On Monday 30 March 1829, Locke gave evidence how, as resident engineer, he had 'set out' the Liverpool & Manchester Railway and that it was being constructed accordingly: 'I am superintending the works and the tunnel under the town of Liverpool';[40] and before numerous Parliamentary Select Committees he stressed that he was in charge until the railway's official opening in September 1830,[41] irrespective of rumours cast about by George

Stephenson to the contrary. Locke wrote to his absent friend Robert Stephenson: 'Liverpool 28 February 1827 . . . I assure you I have had a very busy time since I came here and the present prospect is even more busy — I have upwards of two years labour'd very hard . . .'.[42]

Achievements of Joseph Locke

John Francis' *A History of the English Railway*, published in 1851, sometimes dismissed as biased in favour of George Hudson and his associate George Stephenson,[43] does contain certain facts which shun expediency: Joseph Locke's fame 'dates from Chat Moss'.[44] Described as a swampy tract of great extent, Locke tackled this problematic task in August 1826. George Stephenson had intended 'to traverse Chat Moss on an embankment . . . in his well known horror of steep gradients'. Charles Blacker Vignoles considered: 'it was rather the method by which Stephenson hoped to be able to cross the bog than the impossibility of the thing itself which brought down such denunciations of the proposed agreement in the first Parliamentary contest.'[45] Experienced engineers such as William Chapman knew the problem 'was the limited portion of embankment that was found absolutely necessary'.[46] The large embankment built at Myers Flat on the Stockton & Darlington Railway during the winter of 1821–1822 forever subsided and continually proved an expensive item for the company after the railway's opening in 1825. George Stephenson refused to acknowledge failure, so Locke had to cajole his master into having as little embankment as possible. The persuasion on this matter and other aspects of railway construction over Chat Moss proved to be a drawn-out process.

Fortunately for Locke, there were immediate precedents to follow. A mutual regard quickly developed between the veteran literary figure William Roscoe and the aspiring young engineer determined to improve his education.[47] As a major land owner on Chat Moss, Roscoe had cultivated portions of the bog and had an 'iron road' laid in 1793. About ten years later, Roscoe's innovative steward, Robert Stannard, improved this railway system by designing special trucks to run on his inverted V section wrought-iron rails. This was already at Locke's disposal to assist in the construction of the new railway.

On the Stockton & Darlington Railway bog area, George Stephenson wished to fill the morass with spoil in the mistaken belief that it would eventually stabilise. Roscoe's steward advised the use of larch trees laid in herring-bone fashion as a foundation and thus the floating of the railway over Chat Moss. A controversy arose between the elder Stephenson and Stannard:

> there was great difficulty convincing Stephenson that the raft system was the best, as Stephenson always insisted that if they put spoil enough on the Moss it would find a bottom; but although it did no doubt sometime reach the bottom it did not stay there as the bog had a specific gravity like a quicksand and assisted a flow from side to side . . .[48]

Eventually the chief succumbed to his clerk's influence but, on the success of the operation, the entrepreneur declared the ideas to be his own.[49]

Indeed, George Stephenson had to change course on almost every decision with regard to railway construction. Before the Liverpool & Manchester Railway Bill Select Committee in April 1825, the experienced railway and canal builder, George Leather, criticised the elder Stephenson's lack of overall planning and economic considerations. After citing specific examples, he concluded: 'there were insufficient cuttings on the line of Mr Stephenson's railroad to produce the embankment, therefore ground must be purchased at great expense.'[50] Almost two years after Leather's scathing attack on George Stephenson's intended methods, C B Vignoles voiced the criticism: 'the mode Mr Stephenson proposes to put the works into the course of operation is not the most eligible . . .'.[51] Joseph Locke then induced his master to reject these intentions and substituted his own systematic methods. Beginning with the Olive Mount cutting, Locke used the stone for bridges, block sleepers and ballast, and from this and other cuttings, used spoil for embankments whenever possible. He mentioned in a letter to Robert Stephenson: ' . . . in the Tunnel we are doing very well and I hope very correctly at least I spare neither time nor pains in watching every part of it.'[52] Assistance came from the already experienced contractor John Stephenson, described as being of 'sound judgement, with extraordinary vigorous perseverance'.[53] This quiet unassuming man shunned publicity and, unknown to many, together they evolved new and efficient methods for constructing the 2000 yd Wapping Tunnel, the massive Olive Mount cutting and Broad Green embankment, all of which were on an unprecedented scale in railway engineering.[54] The bond between John Stephenson and Locke was to remain strong.

Locke also had to persuade George Stephenson to drop his fanciful idea of a 'Gothic' viaduct at Sankey.[55] The replacement design, consisting of nine semicircular arches resting on massive splayed piers, became a characteristic Locke design, paralleled, for instance, at Dutton and Barentin.[56]

Achievements of John Rastrick

Concerning the railway mania of 1845, John Francis commented: 'the leading engineers were necessarily at a great premium'. Francis goes on to list the amount of new railway projects they had under their charge: 'Mr Robert Stephenson with thirty-four, Mr Locke with thirty-one . . . Mr Rastrick with seventeen . . . Mr Brunel was said to be connected with fourteen lines.'[57] John Urpeth Rastrick was then sixty-five years old, and had been influential from almost the beginning of the railway revolution. William James anticipated the possibility of a railway network powered by steam locomotives for passengers as well as goods.[58] On 16 September 1822 Lord Redesdale wrote: 'I am well convinced of the advantage to cheapness of conveyance arising from the use of steam engines; and I understand Mr Rastrick to be convinced of the advantage, and he expressed his conviction that in time the engine would be improved.'[59] James had seen a Trevithick locomotive at Camborne in 1803,[60] and subsequently Rastrick was to be the main manufacturer of Richard Trevithick's high-pressure engine.[61] In 1808, one of them was mounted on four wheels to become *Catch-Me-Who-Can*, the first locomotive to have direct drive, the first to have single drive and, attaining a speed of at least 15 mph on a curved track, it can almost be considered the first express passenger engine.[62] A recognised expert on this subject, Rastrick proved to be a formidable witness for the 1825 Liverpool & Manchester Railway Bill.[63] In the face of William James' unfortunate financial predicament, Rastrick ensured at least the first link in James' envisaged railway network with the completion of the Stratford & Moreton Railway in 1826.[64] Rastrick was still eminent when James' vision came to fruition.

One of the most respected and competent of all engineers, Rastrick was the first to give evidence at the Inquiry held on 25 November 1847 into the application of iron to railway structures:[65] 'Of very resolute character, Rastrick always displayed as a witness the greatest shrewdness as well as coolness.'[66] His experience encompassed all aspects of engineering from the role of manufacturer to engineer-in-chief, from cast-iron beams for Buckingham Palace to the magnificent 112 ft span cast-iron bridge at Chepstow, where:[67]

> Economical considerations necessitated the use of part of the foundations of a former bridge, which somewhat interfered with the general symmetry of the appearance of the new bridge; and the immense rise of tide, (48 feet), and its great rapidity, rendered it a work of no ordinary class.[68]

His knowledge of metal properties was second to none. His steam engines, both stationary and locomotive, were renowned for their excellent quality. The awe-inspiring masonry viaducts with apertures in the piers to reduce the weight still stand as monuments to Rastrick's capacity as a structural designer.[69] Perhaps he is best described as an indefatigable perfectionist. Those with whom he was associated regarded him as:

> a man of unremitting application and . . . known to devote whole nights as well as days, to the careful consideration of details of his works, with an energy and minuteness that would have worn out many of his juniors upon which his example produced excellent effect.[70]

Perhaps, however, Rastrick's greatest contribution to the railway revolution was the self-sacrifice of his own interest on two vital occasions, enabling the intentions of Robert Stephenson and Joseph Locke to win the day. For Rastrick would have been the first to acknowledge the essential differences between himself and the two engineering prodigies: Locke and Stephenson were pioneers, a source of inspiration, a driving force. They borrowed, adapted and created anew to become acknowledged leaders of their technological age: 'Ambition is contagious amongst the young',[71] and theirs was a joint ambition to establish an alternative method of national transport against the odds and in the face of adversity. Locke called Robert Stephenson: 'the friend of my youth, the companion of my ripening years, a competitor in the race of life'.[72] Their attributes complemented one another: Stephenson was essentially an inventor, notably of the wrought-iron plate girder[73] and the prototype locomotive;[74] Locke a master of method enabling rapid railway expansion throughout the world. Speed, safety and reliability offered within a unified railway system remained their goal as it would: 'not only confer individual benefits and local advantages, but a great national good, by introducing a system of conveyance throughout the country which is at once easy, safe, expeditious and economical.'[75] The groundwork which had to be done by these two significant railway engineers cannot be over-estimated.

The obstacles posed by George Stephenson

Convinced of the locomotive's superiority over any other form of traction, both Robert Stephenson and Joseph Locke aimed to adopt it as the sole motive power on the railways. Their master prevented this intention until John Rastrick intervened. George Stephenson's main locomotive construction policies can be seen as an avoidance of the need for accuracy, in the interests of short-term economy in construction, maintenance and running costs. Precision was expensive. Immediately after Robert Stephenson left for South America his father ordered the removal of the blast incorporated by his son on the Killingworth locomotives between 1819 and 1822.[76] A frequent visitor to the Stephensons at this time reminisced to Samuel Smiles of:

> . . . the animated and eager discussions . . . with reference to the growing powers of the locomotive engine. The son was even more enthusiastic on the subject than his father . . . Robert would suggest alterations and improvements . . . of the machine. His father, on the contrary, would offer every possible objection, defending the existing arrangements . . .[77]

During the late autumn of 1822 Robert Stephenson drew a series of possible alterations which he labelled on the back 'Locomotive Engine Darlington':[78] a pivoted axle replaces the steam springs, which in practice did not fulfil their function, and this axle also precludes the use of a chain, which is replaced by outside rods to connect the wheels. The witness was right: George Stephenson did 'offer every possible objection' to these innovations but the outside coupling rod was to remain standard. That he preferred the patent components of 1815 and 1816 (which included the chain and the steam spring) is evident from his statements and actions.[79] On 31 December 1824 he declared to his fellow directors that he did not consider that: 'any additions can be made to his former invention of such a moment as to entitle him to sue for a new patent',[80] even though the first Stockton & Darlington locomotive was at least partially constructed, and incorporated Robert Stephenson's new proposals. In fact, George Stephenson and Nicholas Wood continued to promote the chain[81] long after the successful application of outside rods, even though it would stretch with age leading to irregularities 'especially in changing from working back to forward again'.[82] When Robert wished to replace this chain with outside rods, George Stephenson insisted on the introduction of parallel motion to give flexibility and overcome the necessity for exact alignment. These drawings represent a combination of their ideas.

Wishing to create a precision machine combining the cross head and slide bar with the outside coupling rods, Robert Stephenson tried his utmost to persuade his father against the retrograde step by, as usual, artfully citing the current practices of others, but to no avail:

> March 8th 1824. My dear father . . . they have removed the parallel motion . . . as they are found entirely superfluous . . . I have never seen one mathematically true not even in principle — I have found since I left home that even in the case where all the bars are equal it is not true exactly — I know you will doubt this but it is true.[83]

The frustrated engineer left the locomotive scene and signed a three-year contract with the Colombian Mining Association. In June 1824 he wrote to his stepmother: 'I have the satisfaction to say that I never in my whole life spent time to so much advantage as I have done since I left home.'[84]

His replacement as working manager, James Kennedy,[85] completed the first three Stockton & Darlington locomotives with the pivoted axle and outside coupling rods, but followed George Stephenson's wishes with regard to parallel motion; nor did the elder Stephenson authorise the use of the blast principle on these locomotives.[86] Yet Robert Stephenson and Joseph Locke stated: 'The effect of high-pressure Engines is now almost universally admitted to depend, not so much on the size of the cylinder, as upon the quantity of steam which the boiler can generate, and upon a degree of its elasticity.'[87] Like Richard Trevithick before them, they appreciated that 'to produce a profuse generation of steam'[88] by stimulating the fire the blast pipe was essential in order to produce an effective and efficient locomotive. However, using the blast effect led to an apparent 'rapid consumption of fuel'.[89] Removing it from the Killingworth locomotives in 1825 was, as Nicholas Wood put it: 'a means of economising the fuel . . . the engine might then be made to assume the character of a low-pressure engine.'[90] Without the blast, the single-flue Stockton & Darlington locomotives 'sometimes came to a standstill when at work . . . because . . . the steam was generated slowly.'[91] Wood and the elder Stephenson therefore had to increase the heating surface. Wood explained: 'Now by enlarging the flue tube and giving it a double turn through the boiler we have got a sufficiency of steam without [the blast].'[92] They modified at least one Killingworth locomotive from a single to a return flue and also one of the early Stockton & Darlington Railway locomotives, probably no. 4, *Diligence*. Visiting the railway early in 1827, two Prussian engineers noted how: 'another boiler serving for a similar locomotive . . . had . . . a return flue . . . which enters into the chimney, at the end where the fire takes place.'[93]

Although rail breakage remained the major complaint from railway companies, George Stephenson's 1827[94] *Experiment* was of enormous size. Again he applied indirect drive in order to obtain excessive clearances. Nick-named *Old Elbows*, the axle-heavy locomotive was not acceptable until Robert Stephenson modified the machine on his return. At the time his father boasted:

> My Dear Robert . . . I think I told you about my new plan of locomotive it will be a huge job . . . I will not use more than half the coals that has heather to been used, you will think I have some mistaken idea about this but I think not—and you may depend upon it that if you do not get home soon every thing will be at perfecttion and then there will be nothing for you to do or invent . . .[95]

Joseph Locke considered his master's intention to use, by necessity, the low-pressure engine only on a level railway: 'hindered the locomotive's possible advantages . . . This early crotchet of George Stephenson's . . . remained with him to the end and interfered with the first development of the railroad system throwing many difficulties in the way.'[96]

Employed as an independent agent by Lord Ravensworth[97] to construct a railway from a new colliery at Springwell to the staithes at Jarrow and to supply the motive power, Locke was allowed to design the machinery according to his own wishes. For bringing the work to Robert Stephenson & Co. he received £5 and a £10 commission on 30 June 1826.[98] Despite manufacturing constraints, and with an aim for accuracy which was to remain a hallmark of his career, he combined the cross-head and slide-bar with side-rods connecting the wheels for the first time on his two Springwell locomotives.

The application of the blast principle enabled the locomotives to travel on a railway: 'which varied from 1 in 280 to 1 in 80, the average being 1 in 122'.[99] Between January and July 1826, Locke 'had full opportunity of studying the locomotive engine, then comparatively in its infancy and satisfying himself of its capabilities . . . Full confidence was not of course, immediately accorded to the new machine . . .'.[100] Inclines worked by stationary engines were: 'considered indispensable. Locke felt and expressed great confidence in the possibility of working steeper inclines than he was ever permitted to try . . .'.[101]

On the Canterbury & Whitstable and the Liverpool & Manchester Railways, despite the known disruptions caused by a mixture of motive power, George Stephenson insisted on the creation of inclines placed centrally along the lines. He gave a vivid description of his intentions:

> . . . we shall want one steam engine at that place and a nother at near parr moss also one at the top of the tunnal I want these engines to be constantly moveing with an endless Rope so that the locomotive engine can take hold of the Rope and go on without stoping . . . so that the poor [power] of the locomotive assisted by the perment ones will get traffict on in a grand stile . . .[102]

What a recipe for disaster.

As early as October 1822, Robert Stephenson had advised his mentor William James, then chief engineer-designate of the Liverpool & Manchester Railway, not to have a 'fixed engine'[103] on the line. A few weeks later young Robert wrote: ' . . . lay a strong railway down and enjoy the advantage of Locomotive Engines (for no doubt they are an advantage over every other mode hitherto used)'.[104] On Robert Stephenson's return to England in late November 1827[105] the best means of traction for the Liverpool & Manchester Railway: ' . . . was already under discussion and as the time for the opening of the line drew near, the controversy amounted to acrimony.'[106]

The board and the engineering profession distrusted George Stephenson's entrepreneurial proclivities. It soon became apparent that he was sitting on the fence waiting to see the outcome. And whatever they chose, stationary engines or locomotives, he would secure the order for Robert Stephenson & Co.[107] In July 1828, he admitted to Timothy Hackworth that his opinion of locomotives had deteriorated during the past few years.[108] On 6 October 1828 his associate, Company Treasurer

Henry Booth, reported to the directors in favour of stationary haulage engines throughout the line.[109] The private anger of the locomotive enthusiasts can be imagined, and Robert Stephenson and Locke insisted a pro-locomotive report be submitted to the board. Written in Robert's hand and in his style of expression, George Stephenson had no alternative but to present this report on 5 November 1828.[110] He could not afford to lose the services of these two young, highly proficient engineers and, as Samuel Smiles appreciated, despite their difference of opinion with regard to locomotive development, he was: '. . . proud, nevertheless of his son's suggestions and often warmed and excited by his [Robert's] brilliant anticipations of the ultimate triumph of the locomotive.'[111]

Robert Stephenson's report induced the board to employ James Walker and Rastrick to investigate the subject. Rastrick was not an antagonist. At this time he and Robert Stephenson were the only engineers actually manufacturing locomotives to their own designs.[112] A close colleague of Trevithick, Rastrick would have been aware of the constraints being placed on Robert Stephenson, his rival in trade with the United States. In the immediate aftermath of exhilarating discussions with Trevithick,[113] Robert wrote of his locomotive development intentions to a fellow director on 1 January 1828:

> I have been talking a great deal to my father about endeavouring to reduce the size and ugliness of our travelling-engines, by applying the engine either on the side of the boiler or beneath it entirely, somewhat similarly to Gurney's steam-coach. He has agreed to an alteration which I think will considerably reduce the quantity of machinery.[114]

Robert's power of persuasion finally won. There was to be no more indirect drive from Robert Stephenson & Co. but George Stephenson had an almost superstitious aversion to crank axles and prevented his son from following the advice of Trevithick to adopt inside cylinders at this time. This decision resulted in a priority row with James Kennedy,[115] Robert Stephenson's most serious rival in the 1830s. As his actions show, the elder Stephenson still clung to his false notion that 'economy in the consumption of fuel applied to Steam Engines is most efficiently accomplished by allowing combustion to proceed at a low temperature . . .'.

To this philosophy, Locke and Robert Stephenson emphatically declared that they were 'diametrically opposed'.[116] By the application of the blast principle they wished to produce a high-pressure power machine 'in order that simplicity and compactness may be achieved'.[117] In fact the steam road carriage designers were probably in advance of their railway locomotive counterparts. Goldsworthy Gurney commented, 'Many modifications but very few improvements, if any, were made on Trevithick's engine.'[118]

The Rainhill Premium

Twenty years of slow progress served to reduce the rate of full-scale railway promotion. Capitalists continued to pour money into the improving and expanding road and canal networks throughout the 1820s and 1830s. Time might have passed the railways by. Brian Reed appreciated that: 'George Stephenson was never responsible himself for any really noteworthy design, though he held back more than one promising development through caution and obstinacy . . .'[119] and that during Robert Stephenson's absence between 1824 and 1827, there was '. . . even a deterioration in design just when an improvement was needed most decisively'.[120] The great obstacles posed by George Stephenson to locomotive development had to be overcome.

On 21 January 1829 John Rastrick sketched the elder Stephenson's *Experiment*; even after modification the locomotive did not incorporate the blast and he noted the excessive weight — 10 tons 2 cwt.[121] Joseph Locke and Robert Stephenson accompanied him throughout his investigations of the Stockton & Darlington locomotives.[122] They undoubtedly took the opportunity to lobby him with their progressive ideas, especially their intention to create an efficient boiler, capable of producing a maximum amount of steam in a given time. Locke gave his friend essential help and support at this taxing time. Robert Stephenson now had the courage to reject ideas thrust upon him and to introduce a multitubular boiler with a separate firebox.[123] Significantly, a few years later, the Liverpool & Manchester Railway Directors' *Minute Book* records that: 'they were obliged by the tender of Mr Locke's services towards the improvement of the Locomotive Engines and would willingly bear the expenses of the proposed Model . . .'[124] which was for further boiler improvements. Although not displayed working to her best advantage at Leigh, Rastrick[125] also witnessed Robert Stephenson's locomotive

Lancashire Witch, on the drawing board in January 1828[126] and completed after boiler design changes in July 1828.[127] Innovations such as direct drive from the cylinders to the wheels and the application of steel-plate springs for the first time would not have escaped Rastrick's notice;[128] indeed, he noted the weights of component parts.[129] When the ensuing report of Walker and Rastrick recommended stationary engines as being the most reliable at that time,[130] they in fact gave Stephenson and Locke both a chance and a challenge. Walker suggested 'something of a premium . . . to encourage and draw attention of Engine-makers to the subject'.[131]

In 1822, Lord Redesdale had written of Rastrick being convinced of the locomotive's advantages and expressing a hope that it would be improved.[132] Consequently the report also stated there were 'grounds for expecting improvements in the construction and work of the locomotive'.[133]

Understanding the motives of Rastrick, the two young locomotive enthusiasts consolidated their ideas and used the official report as an excuse to issue a 'counter report'.[134] They submitted this pro-locomotive report to the board on 20 April 1829.[135] Robert Stephenson recalled: 'I believe I furnished the facts and arguments, Locke put them into shape.'[136] Here was a second written argument to oppose the notions of the elder Stephenson and Nicholas Wood and to uphold Robert Stephenson and Locke's long-held view of the locomotive's great potential on the application of the blast.[137] They also advocated its flexibility as an independent agent: 'we cannot but express our decided conviction that a system that necessarily involved by a single accident, the stoppage of the whole, is totally unfitted for a public railway.'[138]

The near-contemporary author John Francis was aware how Rastrick's recommendations, with the added weight of Stephenson and Locke's facts and arguments, led to the decision to offer a premium of £500 to the owner of a locomotive which on a certain day should perform certain conditions in the most satisfactory manner. Announced on 25 April 1829, the stipulations were tailor-made for the young engineers' design intent: a six-wheel engine with water not to exceed six tons — 'a machine of less weight will be preferred . . . if reduced to 4½ tons it could be placed on 4 wheels.'[139] John Rastrick considered that:

'locomotives weighing more than eight tons could not be conveniently used to get a speed of more than ten miles an hour. I am decidedly of the opinion that fifteen miles per hour on a railroad may be travelled in perfect safety, both to goods and passengers.' An answer, considered theoretically conclusive, from Mr Robert Stephenson and Mr Locke, was followed by the determination to try the locomotive.[140]

Rastrick now knew that the possibility of speed combined with undisrupted travel on a private network was the railway's best promotion point. Having offered precise recommendations, he thus attempted to eliminate the possibility of a massive low-tech machine being acceptable for the proposed premium. Speed was never a consideration of George Stephenson's[141] and Nicholas Wood reiterated his business associate's position when he criticised the speed enthusiasts' stance, anticipating travelling at rates of: '. . . 12, 16, 18 or 20 miles an hour; nothing could do more harm towards their adoption or general improvement than the promulgation of such nonsense.'[142] A sarcastic article likening the danger of death from flying fragments of burst locomotive boilers with being fired at by one of Congreve's ricochet rockets, may well have inspired Robert Stephenson to call his Premium engine *Rocket*, as a slap in the face to the anti-speed lobby.

In April 1829, Rastrick was constructing three locomotives at his works. Bound for America, they weighed six tons, had steel plate springs, the blast and the most advanced boiler at that time[143] which: 'in economy, speed, and accuracy of workmanship, equalled if it did not excel, any engine . . . hitherto produced.'[144] Essentially a trial of the fittest, the Rainhill Premium could possibly have been his, although perhaps he would have been hard pressed to reduce the component parts of his *Stourbridge Lion* type to 4½ tons. Timothy Hackworth did attempt to lighten his six-wheel *Royal George*, weighing 12 tons 7 cwts 2 st with water, and almost succeeded.[145] But Rastrick's locomotives incorporated indirect 'Grasshopper' drive and were destined to be a dead end. The many moving parts rattled and shook[146] and were ill-suited to high speeds. However, Rastrick had the means and the experience to develop Trevithick's *Catch-Me-Who-Can* high-pressure engine which he had manufactured prolifically for the inventor.[147] Indeed, for his Premium entry, Robert Stephenson borrowed the simple elegance of Trevithick's 1802 patent Steam Road Carriage[148] with direct drive to the large pair of driving wheels. Appreciating the total design concept of Robert Stephenson, Rastrick subjugated thoughts of a reward. He never built another locomotive.

By contrast, Timothy Hackworth had an ardent determination to win. But the design of his *Sans Pareil* was retrograde, nor did the locomotive fulfil the conditions.[149] The return flue combined with a contracted blast pipe was not efficient: 'and was decidedly overrated by him; in fact he carried the contraction to such an extent that nearly half the fuel was thrown out of the chimney unconsumed, as many can testify who witnessed the experiments at Rainhill.'[150] High speeds were rendered impossible by the inherent return flue feature requiring the driver and fireman to be at the opposite ends of the locomotive. The vertical outside cylinders pounded directly onto the wheels, increasing the possibility of rail breakage and causing severe oscillation. J G H Warren commented: 'The success of the *Sans Pareil* would probably have encouraged a return to the vertical cylinder with direct drive which had been definitely abandoned by Robert Stephenson in 1828; for this reason alone it is perhaps fortunate she failed.'[151] Robert Stephenson's *Rocket* was a prototype; his formula did not break down upon the introduction of new ideas.[152]

The authors of the pro-locomotive 'facts and arguments' decided to add a section about the Rainhill trials and publish their report. George Stephenson, concerned about his image, urged, as the pamphlet was passing through the press in February 1830, 'that the title page should bear his name and his name only'.[153] As Robert Stephenson had written and presented short pro-locomotive reports to the board in his father's name, Locke conceded 'with great reluctance'.[154] After all, the joy of success should be sufficient reward. The text of the first and original section was not altered: 'The Report drawn up by Joseph Locke and Robert Stephenson had demonstrated theoretically the superiority of the locomotive'[155] and the *Rocket* had proved it.

The Grand Junction Railway

Another notion of George Stephenson's had yet to be eliminated and again Rastrick played a crucial role. Although the practice of acting as sole general contractor for the whole of the Liverpool & Manchester Railway had been condemned by Thomas Telford,[156] George Stephenson still intended to continue with this system on what became the world's first long-distance railway — the Grand Junction.[157] Not only was this considered to be 'highly improper and thwart with opportunities for abuse',[158] but it led to gross inefficiencies wasting both manpower and materials, the line not being completed on time and exceeding the original estimate.[159] Without Robert Stephenson's precise instructions and contract letting on the Stockton & Darlington Railway, it took John Dixon and Thomas Storey almost eighteen months to complete the remaining three miles of main line between March 1824 and September 1825.[160] Also, during Robert's absence, the construction of intended branch lines to make the railway viable was extremely slow; consequently Edward Pease had personally to fund the railway until it became fully operational.[161] Even the elder Stephenson's staunchest henchman, Dixon, admitted that when:

> The Company finds most of the materials and keeps the railroad in order which adds considerably to the expense . . . it is considered to do it cheaper by piecework; it is a great deal more trouble . . . but I have never known any railway done for the estimate that was made for it.[162]

To build a railway on time and within the initial estimate was to be Locke's great achievement.[163] Both he and Robert Stephenson had to abandon methods forced upon them under the auspices of George Stephenson & Son and against their known former practices.[164] On 25 January 1830, Robert Stephenson explained to a fellow director how he could do the work of engineer-in-chief to a number of companies at the same time: 'I should divide my attention and I see no difficulty in doing that, when I have a confidential assistant at each place to see that my plans are carefully and strictly attended to. . .'.[165] The greater the preliminary planning on Stephenson and Locke's part, the more they could delegate with confidence; they had already begun to train assistants. Although by the end of 1830, the advantage of connecting two industrial towns by railway was more than evident, extending the system proved to be another matter. Because of the stigma attached to that 'most unholy alliance to George Stephenson & Son'[166], railway Bills submitted under that establishment were either thrown out or passed into the hands of other engineers between 1831 and 1833.[167] It appeared that all the initial survey work done by Locke and Robert Stephenson was in vain. The failure of the London & Birmingham Bill in 1832 caused Lord Wharncliffe to sympathise: 'My young friend, don't take this to heart. The decision is against you; but you have made such a display of power that *your future is made for life*.'[168] Both Robert Stephenson and the board gained confidence from Rastrick, who, aware of the young engineer's innovative designs, declared:

> Let nothing deter you from executing the work in the most substantial manner and on the most scientific principles so that it may serve as a model for all future railways and become the wonder and admiration of Posterity. There is not anything but what a large spirited company like yours can achieve.[169]

The Bill was resubmitted and passed through both Houses. On 30 September 1833, Robert Stephenson signed in his own right as engineer-in-chief.[170] A clause in George Stephenson & Son's constitution enabled Robert Stephenson to resign as director if he so wished.[171] Matters were not so easy for the chief clerk, Joseph Locke.

Locke began to survey a route connecting the Liverpool & Manchester Railway with Birmingham in late 1829. Asked by another railway company to survey an alternative route, Robert Stephenson wrote on 17 December 1829: 'It is adverse to my feelings to be connected with any undertaking which might interfere with Mr Locke's views, as his kindness to my father has been very great.'[172] On this railway, Locke wished to apply his cost-effective proposals and thus win shareholders' confidence to invest in the expansion of the system. In this task he was aided by Rastrick, whose notebooks bear witness to the intricate detailing that he was prepared to do.[173] At this stage Locke diplomatically informed his titular chief of their proposals: 'Rastrick wishes to calculate the Bridges separately as well on our part of the line as his own; . . . it is not withstanding the safest plan. I shall be glad to hear from you . . .'.[174]

William Mackenzie also helped Locke to prepare costings and submitted estimates of structures and excavations to the young engineer on 20 and 25 March 1833.[175] Publicly questioned as to whether or not George Stephenson fulfilled any engineering function, Locke replied in the negative: 'The original parliamentary estimate was prepared by Mr Rastrick and myself for the whole line . . . I signed it myself . . . Mr Rastrick and I made the estimates jointly as engineers . . . In 1833 at the time the Bill was passed . . .'.[176] Rastrick then unselfishly withdrew all interest in the Grand Junction Railway.

In May 1833, '. . . when the appointment on the line came to be made, Locke was inclined to expect very much, Stephenson was inclined to give very little,'[177] and a compromise was reached. Given the northern section, Locke had prepared and issued tenders for all the contracts by 25 September 1834, the first two being let to John Stephenson. Left to organise the southern section, George Stephenson's incompetence was revealed. Discrepancies in the calculations induced the board to call for Locke's intervention to revise the specifications, resulting in the joint appointment of Stephenson and Locke as engineers.[178] The choice of rails proved another stumbling block. Although the elder Stephenson appeared prepared to authorise tests on various rail types, in reality he would not abandon his business ties with Michael Longridge who produced the fish-bellied 'T' section rails.[179] As early as September 1832, Locke had lobbied Pease to influence the nominal chief in favour of his own 'I' section rail and chair. Pease's written response had no effect.[180] Finally, George Stephenson resigned on 16 September 1835.[181]

Of Locke it was said that he 'possessed peculiar qualities of mind which secured for him the confidence of capitalists, by whom the construction of the Grand Junction was entrusted to him.'[182] Locke gave precise specifications which enabled contractors to give him an almost faultless service and therefore he could create much larger divisions than any engineer had dared to use before: 'Assistant engineers and contractors used to complain bitterly that young Locke used to walk them off their legs.'[183] His enthusiasm inspired others to work and nothing escaped his critical eye. As was his custom on the Liverpool & Manchester Railway he moved in extra labour to speed up the work at problematic sections, maintaining double shift working and economically using stone from cuttings for bridges. Opened on 6 July 1837, the Grand Junction was the first railway to be constructed on time and within the original estimate. Locke then made every effort to run a comfortable, safe and efficient railway. He had introduced his design of heavy, durable 'I' section rail, mounted on wooden transverse sleepers, which became standard in Britain for a hundred years. When later given a choice, the public's preference for Locke's method of rail construction won the day; the smoother ride on his railways contrasted sharply with the jars and jolts experienced from the rails mounted on stone blocks or longitudinal sleepers. After establishing a company locomotive factory at Crewe, Locke stated: 'It was desirable both for the facility of working and economy in manufacture, that the different parts such as wheels, axles etc should be made uniform and that there should be identity between leading dimensions.'[184]

Putting his ideals of order, mathematical accuracy and economic efficiency into practice, Locke instigated a new era of locomotive manufacturing. Even in 1860 colleagues considered that his method of rationalised production had not yet been fully appreciated.[185] The Grand Junction remained with Locke, 'as the very shadow of his presence', the epitome of his 'reputation for firmness of will, integrity of purpose, ingenuity of resource and skill in appliances'.[186] When other engineers faltered, his services were called upon.[187]

Achievements of John Stephenson

To connect London and Newcastle by railway communication had been a favourite object of Robert Stephenson's ambition.[188] Inspired by the prophecies of Thomas Grey and William James,[189] he took his route northwards from the London & Birmingham Railway to Derby, Rotherham, York, Ferryhill and Pelaw. The major contractor was John Stephenson, whose expertise undoubtedly relieved the young engineer of some of the strain.

After the Grand Junction debacle, George Stephenson's retirement from all things railway had been anticipated.[190] The elder Stephenson thought otherwise. In an attempt to repair his father's self-esteem, Robert Stephenson dutifully offered him sanctuary within his own engineering consultancy and asked two of his employees, G P Bidder[191] and T L Gooch,[192] to play an engineering liaison role with the entrepreneur. Remembering the experiences of Hugh Steel and William Allcard,[193] Thomas Gooch showed a reluctance to be joint engineer-in-chief on the Manchester & Leeds Railway.[194] Gooch accepted, realising Robert Stephenson's intention to take the engineering initiative by employing Francis Whishaw[195] to do the survey and for the structural design work to follow his own former practices.[196] Gooch had the responsibility of letting the contracts and supervising the construction. Even so there are indications of inefficiency. Robert had to stand as arbiter;[197] the Summit Tunnel's original contractors Evans and Copeland proved inadequate and they had to be superseded in March 1839 by John Stephenson, who signed all the existing drawings of the tunnel as constructed.[198] Despite the bravado of George Stephenson, it is not too difficult to appreciate who should receive credit for the tunnel's success. There was little love lost between the two namesakes acting as contractor and engineer. On 31 October 1841 the elder Stephenson wrote to Thomas Gooch:

> I have been pressed both by John Stephenson & Evans to have their affairs settled with the Manchester & Leeds Railway Co . . . I do not wish to have anything to do with the settlement of John Stephenson's affairs . . . I suppose you are aware he has got Wheeler to act for him . . . and it would be much better for you to try to settle it yourself, I am quite aware of the unpleasant situation in which you are placed, the works having so far exceeded the estimate.[199]

And on 4 November 1841:

> I beg you will not consider that I wish you to give in to Stephenson one sixpence more than is due to him . . .[200]

This in spite of the fact George Stephenson had earlier thought John would waive the money owed to him 'provided the thing was settled'.[201] That the costs of this railway far exceeded the original estimate was Gooch's fault, not the contractor's. Nor was Gooch a reliable witness in his retrospective manuscript memoirs on many issues.[202]

Undoubtedly John Stephenson had been prepared to step in and save the Stephenson reputation for the sake of Robert Stephenson. On 2 April 1839 the contractor organised 'a subscription . . . for the purpose of presenting to ROBERT STEPHENSON a TESTIMONIAL of the high estimation in which he is held . . . no Subscription to exceed five pounds . . . (signed) John Stephenson, Chairman.'[203]

The engineer-in-chief of the Birmingham & Derby Junction, North Midland, Sheffield & Rotherham, York & North Midland and Manchester & Leeds railways received a candelabrum and dinner service, designed and manufactured expressly for the occasion, at the Albion Hotel, Aldersgate Street, London,[204] on what was then thought to be his birthday, 16 November 1839. George Stephenson '. . . was in the decline of life . . . and saw his son there publicly honoured, whilst he himself had been comparatively unnoticed'.[205]

Robert Stephenson had been compromised by his father's business promotion tactics. To serve minerals, not men, he took a circuitous route northwards to the Scottish capital and for the sake of immediate economy used existing railways as well.[206] Once freed from the same shackles, Locke was able to choose a direct route to Glasgow and Edinburgh.

He surveyed the line himself within months of George Stephenson's enforced resignation from the Grand Junction. In 1836 Locke published a report: *London & Glasgow Railway Through Lancashire.*[207] It represents one of the '. . . greatest feats in railway planning and . . . demonstrates the breadth and clarity of his thinking and his extraordinary ability to sift and analyse essential facts from a mass of data'.[208] Locke's ability to assess the lie of the land and select the best route over such formidable terrain as Shap Fell and Beattock Summit remained unrivalled. He selected the most direct railway: '. . . embracing as many towns as possible and constructing the railway according to the potential traffic'.[209] He would construct 'a dead level on lines of abundant traffic',[210] but when the line crossed sparsely populated areas with little industry, he then kept structures to a minimum. On the Caledonian Railway it was noted in 1847 that the gradients varied from level to 1 in 200, there were no tunnels upon the line and the curves were slight.[211] Locke chose John Stephenson to execute this route.[212]

After the Lancaster & Preston section was opened in June 1840, the rest of the railway remained in abeyance until 1844. Meanwhile, John Stephenson lent his services to John Rastrick, offering his experience in tunnel and cutting construction at Chorley on the Bolton & Preston Railway, completed in December 1841; also to Robert Stephenson on the Northampton & Peterborough Railway. Then came John Stephenson & Co.'s arduous assignment as sole contractor for the last link connecting the great Scottish cities to London in 1844. That Locke refused to tender for the role of contractor caused the Caledonian Company concern. He did not flinch: the trust held between engineer and contractor was absolute.[213]

Based at Murrayfield House, Edinburgh, John Stephenson's partners were William Mackenzie and Thomas Brassey.[214] Surviving documents make it possible to surmise that for the most part John Stephenson took the initiative concerning Locke's railways in the north of England and Scotland whilst Mackenzie was in charge of the Company's affairs on the Continent and Brassey remained in London. Likewise, Locke took up residence at Moffat and sent his nephew William Locke to live in Paris while his business partner John Errington managed matters generally in London. It says much for the exuberant engineer's sense of purpose that the partners of John Stephenson & Co. tolerated Locke's fluctuating temperament. They all clearly lived for their work. John Stephenson was prepared to risk his fortune for the sake of keeping the railway's costs within Locke's original estimate and drove himself to the limit to finish within the allotted time. Mackenzie wrote in his diary: 'Wednesday 20 October 1847. I went to Edinbro today . . . Mr Brassey arrived in the afternoon. The affair about Stephenson's money matters have made me feel very uncomfortable and such contracts as far as I can Judge are most ridiculously low at most ruinous prices.'[215] On the next day at 'a great Directors' Meeting' the resolve was made to finish the line by 16 December. Three days later Mackenzie expressed his fear of John Stephenson being on the verge of bankruptcy. Locke had appealed to a Caledonian director on his friend's behalf:

> I have made another examination of the Line which . . . I found in a very satisfactory state . . . and prodigious efforts have been made by the Contractors during the last fortnight . . . in order to have it ready . . . I hope it will be in your power to supply them with *means* to enable them to do so.[216]

On 5 December 1847 John Stephenson wrote a reassuring letter concerning 'the forward state of the works . . . I shall have an Engine brought on the line from Carlisle to Edinburgh'[217] to arrange a trip for the directors. The brave man's letter shows no hint of personal strain. A vivid description concerning the construction problems of this railway through bogs and millstone grit was recorded by James Day,[218] one of Locke's assistant engineers.

At the age of fifty-four, John Stephenson died at Rotherham on 8 July 1848 whilst conducting a maintenance contract visit to Robert Stephenson's North Midland Railway. A eulogy records John Stephenson's 'high moral and religious sentiments, not only in private but amongst his workmen. Few men lived and died more respected.'[219] This was a sentiment verified in the Caledonian Company records.[220] It took a number of years to settle the John Stephenson & Co. partnership affairs. After the various railway companies had paid their debts, John Stephenson's estate was worth £90,672, but he did not reap the financial rewards of his vast labours.[221]

Credit where credit is due

However competent John Stephenson was at meeting the requirements of his contracts, he knew that without the prime moving force of the engineer-in-chief he would not be doing the work at all. Associates and employees ought to be acknowledged for the part they play in a project but the role of designers and decision-makers must also be recognised. L T C Rolt stated: 'To seek to transfer credit from designers to executants, however able, is to introduce an element of futile argument which can only reduce the history of invention to nonsense.'[222]

Concerning the Tring cutting, Thomas Roscoe wrote soon after the official opening of the London & Birmingham Railway:

> To Mr S S Bennett, the assistant engineer, the merit is due to having executed, in its most perfect manner, the conceptions of the master mind of him who designed this vast effort of skill and enterprise. Accordingly the name of Robert Stephenson will, in after years, be recorded as one of the greatest men of the age in which he lived.[223]

Scott Russell expressed the same sentiment with regard to the wrought-iron plate girder principle. Whilst appreciating:

> . . . the talent of accomplished scientific assistants whose minds Robert Stephenson had cultivated with sedulous care and attention . . . I am quite sure that the very men to whose labours Mr Stephenson was most indebted were the very men who would now say — it was Stephenson alone that did it and that without him they could not have been able to contribute anything.[224]

Beyond the carefully nurtured self-effacing public image, Robert Stephenson was nevertheless proud. Referring to the *Rocket* locomotive design he said:

> I think it perfectly ridiculous to go into the absurd and ridiculous stories which some writers have hatched up about my father's conduct with the *Rocket* . . . I had charge personally of the Engine . . . Whatever was done to the Engine was done under my own eye and direction.[225]

His chief draughtsman confirmed: 'Having made the original drawings under Mr Robert Stephenson, I can bear witness to the care and judgement bestowed by him on every detail.'[226] Robert Stephenson's initiative is revealed in his letters dating from 3 August to 5 September 1829: 'The Wheels I am arranging so as to throw 2 Tuns upon the large wheels in order to get friction upon the rail.'[227] There were no two-way communications between the *Rocket*'s designer and constructor in Newcastle and the other two owners in Liverpool, only polite, dutiful reports from Robert Stephenson to Henry Booth, who was instructed to: 'Please inform my father and Mr Locke the progress we have made.' The only questions asked concerned the Rainhill Trial stipulations and conditions; the answers came via Locke, the sole known correspondent to the inventor during the Premium engine's construction.[228]

When James Kennedy attempted to claim priority for the introduction of inside cylinders to railway locomotives, Robert Stephenson entered the debate: ' . . . the working drawings of the *Planet*. . . had been made and the engine constructed under my direction without reference to, or knowledge of the *Liverpool*.'[229] He went on to explain how he derived the ideas for maximum heat conservation, and the 'economy of fuel' from Richard Trevithick. Had he been given a free rein, he would have introduced an inside cylinder locomotive immediately after his return from South America.[230]

Locke was equally adamant about his locomotive design role: 'the inside cylinder had necessarily a crank axle and we had so many breakages on the Grand Junction that it was not only a source of great expense but of danger . . . to avoid this . . . we adopted a change which I have suggested.'[231] The change involved a significant design modification: placing the outside cylinders within a double frame. The locomotive came to be known generally as the Crewe type. Locke's design was the first reliable alternative to Robert Stephenson's 1833 inside cylinder *Patentee* type. Contemporaries recognised the innovations as Locke's; his employees, Allan, Trevithick and Buddicom, fulfilled his instructions: 'Locke was the designer of "the Crewe engine" in which the several parts were made with mathematical accuracy and were capable of fitting indifferently any engine.'[232]

The Dee bridge disaster of May 1847 left Robert Stephenson vulnerable to the unscrupulous,[233] for although he had not personally designed this truss girder bridge,[234] he was nevertheless responsible as engineer-in-chief to the Chester & Holyhead Railway. Then William Fairbairn published declarations of initiative for the tubular girder principle.[235] Placed in an unenviable defensive position, Robert Stephenson responded with his own publication, saying how the success of the project:

> . . . demands of me a public acknowledgement to Mr Fairbairn I am indebted for the zeal with which he entered upon the experimental investigation, for the confidence he displayed in the success of my design . . . To Mr Hodgkinson for devising and carrying out a series of experiments . . . enabling me to proceed with more confidence . . . To Mr Edwin Clark the resident engineer for the important assistance he has rendered me in strictly

sanctioning the results of every experiment before . . . I finally decided upon the form and dimensions of the structure or upon any mode of procedure . . . I cannot close this statement . . . without expressing my regret . . . that one of the gentlemen . . . endeavoured to enhance his own claims by detracting from the credit fairly due to those with whom he has been associated in this great work.[236]

Joseph Locke squashed Fairbairn's priority claims when he gave the evidence:

In fact wrought-iron plate for beams of steam engines . . . have been used very long and I think carrying it out to a large extent is a very judicious plan. I have several plans on a smaller scale of wrought-iron ones which I use and prefer for moderate spans to cast iron.[237]

Wrought-iron load-bearing frames had indeed been used on Robert Stephenson's *Northumbrian* of June 1830.[238] Locke then developed this frame for his outside cylinder Crewe-type locomotive and constructed wrought-iron plate girders for short bridges but his method of testing was empirical: he placed locomotives nose to tail on the bridges. Whereas, in order to construct large spans, Robert Stephenson instigated unprecedented calculations and experiments between 1845 and 1847 and for the first time structural engineering became a scientifically based profession. His colleagues unequivocally called him 'the inventor of the tubular girder principle'.[239]

Scott Russell considered Robert Stephenson to be the 'greatest risk taker'[240] of his generation; though, like most sensitive creators, he lived on a knife-edge of discovery and felt as if he would 'crack like an egg-shell'.[241] Doubts gave way to certainty because he: 'never devised a scheme of which he did not well consider the practical details'.[242] Such was Robert Stephenson's and Locke's experience with the design and construction of both the locomotives and structures that even if they only drew an outline executed to scale,[243] they would have been well aware of how the total concept would come into being, however much they delegated. The word 'design' can be misinterpreted. A calculator, draughtsman or resident engineer can be working at 'the design', doing component drawings, checking figures or deciding on construction methods.[244] George Phipps did the necessary drawings for *Rocket* — but he was obeying the instructions of Robert Stephenson.[245] Nor does a signature on a highly detailed structural drawing or painting signify authorship or inspiration. For instance, after the Barentin Viaduct collapsed William Mackenzie recorded: 'Today I met Locke . . . he looked sad and was in low spirits after I found him . . . in Neumann's office . . . engaged in making a Plan for reconstructing Barentin viaduct . . . I found Mr Tite making the drawing.'[246] The architect William Tite was permanently employed by Locke primarily for the purpose of designing impressive station buildings, his other function being to execute detailed architectural drawings of structures. Both Robert Stephenson and Joseph Locke also employed artists to do oil paintings of intended important structures for promotion purposes.[247] Concerning contractors, Robert Stephenson produced tight instructions[248]. Having done his outline design, Locke preferred to trust 'manufacturers to mix the iron' because of their 'daily habit' in the trade.[249] Delegation of initiative to contractors ought not to deny credit to the author of a structure's outline. Locke was known to have designed the wrought-iron bowstring girder to span Commercial Road, London, and cast-iron arch bridges across the River Thames.[250] His contemporaries recognised him as an eminent structural designer: 'In every case they are exactly fitted to the places they occupy; and in the same manner his bridges over the Thames and the Seine are distinguished for their adaption to their position. The lightness and simplicity of their construction and the elegance of their design . . .'.[251] Locke returned a similar compliment to his friend: 'Robert Stephenson achieved some of the greatest works of art which have been witnessed in our day, he obtained at the same time an eminence in the scientific world rarely reached by any practical professional man.'[252]

Engineers used publications such as those by Brees and Weale in order to promote their significant designs, some of which were of far-reaching innovative importance. There was no doubt in the engineer Brees' mind as to who was the originator of the first-known all wrought-iron roof span known as the Euston Truss: Robert Stephenson.[253] Also, at a dinner given on Newcastle Central Station in his honour, Robert stated: 'Beyond drawing the outline, I have no right to claim any credit for the works above where we now sit. Upon Mr Harrison the whole responsibility of execution has fallen . . .'.[254] The elegance of this roof structure has never been surpassed; it is a product of Robert Stephenson's experience and practice.

During the mid 1860s, the technical railway revolution was almost complete and standardisation had set in. The engineer Francis Conder recalled how: 'In 1833, works which are now regarded with comparative indifference, engaged the very maximum care of those who had the responsibility of designing them . . .'.[255]

The four great engineers John Rastrick, John Stephenson, Robert Stephenson and Joseph Locke, despite their very different attributes, had one objective in common: to establish a national railway network. The instigation of this vision almost totally absorbed their lives. At certain critical times, they were an essential and decisive prop to each other.

Acknowledgements

I would like to thank Adrian Jarvis and Antony Hall-Patch for their helpful discussions and encouragement; also John Crompton and Robert Stephenson Roper for several references.

Notes and references

If a manuscript has been correctly transcribed in a publication, this reference is given for ease of access.

1 'Obituary of Joseph Locke', *The Times* (21 September 1860)

2 *Minutes of Proceedings of the Institution of Civil Engineers*, XIX (1860), pp1–3, 176–82, XX (1861), pp1–4, 141–48; Francis, J, *A History of the English Railway*, vols I and II (London: Longman & Green, 1851), I, pp196–201, 234–36; Devey, J, *A Life of Joseph Locke* (London: Richard Bentley, 1862), pp90–111, 117–31, 132–44, 155–84, 233–46; *Railway Post Office Directory*, 1848; Jeaffreson, J C, *The Life of Robert Stephenson*, vols I and II (London: Longman & Green, 1864), I, pp220, 239, 259, II, pp130, 184. In II, pp252–53, Jeaffreson incorrectly states that Robert Stephenson's voyage to Christiania (Oslo) in August 1859 was to attend a celebratory banquet for the opening of the first Norwegian railway. In fact the railway had been open for some time, and problems had arisen involving G P Bidder (resident engineer) which necessitated Robert Stephenson standing as arbiter in his own home. Discrepancies arose with regard to contracts and Bidder declared: 'It is quite clear I must give up railway making.' The Norwegian government would have preferred stone rather than wooden bridges so Robert as engineer-in-chief gave the defence: 'stone bridges were never contemplated for this Railway because I made the original Estimate for the Norwegian Government' (*The Norwegian Trunk Railway, before Robert Stephenson Esq. MP. Arbiter, 34 Gloucester Square, Hyde Park, 11 September 1856*, p16—ten copies were printed). Dr Broch's copy is strewn with notes which he dates December 1857. Jeaffreson does give a correct version of the railway's history (II, pp130–31): in 1846 Robert had been approached to 'unite Christiania with the Moisen Lake'. Four years later he was 'retained as Engineer-in-Chief': during the autumn of 1851, 1852 and 1854, he 'superintended the operations'. His visit of August 1859 was to appease: the feast was given not in celebration but conciliation.

3 Evidence of Joseph Locke, *Report of the Commissioners Appointed to Inquire into the Application of Iron to Railway Structures* (London: W Clowes & Sons, 1849), p340

4 Devey, J, p25

5 Evidence of Robert Stephenson, *Evidence Taken Before a Committee of the House of Commons on the Newcastle & Carlisle Railway Bill* (Newcastle upon Tyne: W M Boag, 1829), p127

6 Even after being employed as a contractor for ten years, John Stephenson still called himself an engineer, e.g. in the Baptism Register, St Elphins, Warrington, concerning his four daughters born 1831, 1835 and 1836, and on the document 'Adminstration of the effects of George Stephenson'.

7 Foster, F, 'Memoir', *Proc. ICE*, XII (1853), pp157–59

8 Jeaffreson, J C, I, pp34, 46

9 Jeaffreson, J C, I, p47

10 *Gateshead Observer* (19 August 1848), George Stephenson's speech on 18 June 1844: 'He [Robert Stephenson] got an appointment as underviewer . . . when I got leave to go from Killingworth to lay down a railway at Hetton.' Circumstantial evidence: contrary to his father's locomotive development ideas, Robert

Stephenson modified the Killingworth locomotive by re-introducing the blast and reducing the weight (Warren, J G H, *A Century of Locomotive Building by Robert Stephenson & Company* (Newcastle upon Tyne: Andrew Reid, 1923), p25). Also pp96–97, Letter, W Hutchinson to Robert Stephenson, 2 May 1845: 'I have now served you twenty four years' (i.e. 1821 at Killingworth). Public Record Office, Kew, RAIL 667/274: Robert Stephenson was still in charge of Killingworth Engine Workshop in April 1822 even though his employment as underviewer had ceased.

11 Jeaffreson, J C, I, p53

12 Jeaffreson, J C, I, p55

13 Jeaffreson, J C, I, p55

14 Jeaffreson, J C, I, p53; A bound collection of manuscripts entitled *Early Railway History*, I, p23, Newcastle upon Tyne Central Library

15 Public Record Office, RAIL 667/278

16 Jeaffreson, J C, I, pp53–54; Public Record Office, RAIL 667/274

17 Evidence of Robert Stephenson, *Evidence Taken Before a Committee of the House of Commons on the Newcastle & Carlisle Railway Bill*, p128, '. . . sometimes a week, sometimes a fortnight.'

18 Jeaffreson, J C, I, pp55, 59–60. Correspondence reveals an inconsistency of dates concerning George Stephenson's necessary trip to London. He should have left by 5 April 1823, but his own intention was to delay for a fortnight or three weeks. By that time Robert was able to leave Edinburgh and usher his survey through both Houses: 'Before making his first public appearance as Engineer of the Stockton & Darlington Railway, Robert Stephenson . . . '.

19 *Robert Stephenson & Co. Minute Book*, pp1–4, Science Museum; Warren, J G H, pp52–57

20 Evidence of Robert Stephenson, *Evidence Taken Before a Committee of the House of Commons on the Newcastle & Carlisle Railway Bill*, p128

21 Trevithick, F, *The Life of Richard Trevithick*, vols I and II (London: Spoon, 1872), II, p273

22 Trevithick, F, II, p272

23 Smiles, S, *Lives of the Engineers*, vols I–III (London: Murray, 1862), III, p59

24 Evidence of Robert Stephenson, *Evidence Taken Before a Committee of the House of Commons on the Newcastle & Carlisle Railway Bill*, pp126, 128

25 Evidence of Robert Stephenson, *Report of the Commissioners Appointed to Inquire into the Application of Iron to Railway Structures*, p332

26 Stephenson, R, *Diary 1834*, Science Museum

27 Jeaffreson, J C, I, p240

28 Swanwick, F, 'Memoir', *Proc. ICE*, LXXXV (1886), p405; Haworth, V, 'A case study: George Stephenson 1781–1848', in Jarvis, A and Rees, P (eds), *Nineteenth Century Business Ethics* (Liverpool: National Museums and Galleries on Merseyside and University of Liverpool, 1993), pp19–20

29 Evidence of George Stephenson, *Minutes of Evidence taken before the Lords Committees on the London & Brighton Railway Bill* (ordered to be printed 7 July 1836), pp162–63, House of Lords Record Office. Witnesses giving evidence to Parliamentary Select Committees were not under oath; however, no mercy was shown by cross-examining counsel: 'Most vehement abuse was bestowed upon Mr Stephenson' (Francis, J, I, p105).

30 Austin, A, *Autobiography* (London: Macmillan, 1911), p16; *Proc. ICE*, XIX (1860), pp177–78, XX (1861), pp142–43

31 Austin, A, p17; *Proc. ICE*, LXXXV (1886), pp403–4

32 Austin, A, p16

33 Rolt, L T C, *George & Robert Stephenson* (London: Longman, 1960), pp105–25, 213–14, 250. With so much evidence against George Stephenson being able to survey or organise the construction of a new line — not even the Hetton Colliery Railway, engineered by his brother Robert (1788–1837) — Rolt on the one hand admits the facts but then offers the hypothetical information: 'In preliminary reconnaissance he was brilliant . . . grasping what was best from an engineering point of view . . . Traffic potential . . . as a future link in some route.' This is a mirror image conclusion and Rolt has to contradict himself: 'his mind could never grasp the implications of his visions in terms of administration and finance' (p270). What 'vision' did George ever have, other than to 'point out' a proposed new railway to an employee such as Locke, Swanwick, Bourne, from his coach? (and usually to make sure his coach was seen — he looked and played the part). (Haworth, V, p21).

34 Locke, J, *Contract of Employment* (11 January 1825), manuscript held in the Institution of Mechanical Engineers
35 Letter, Joseph Locke to Robert Stephenson, 25 November 1825, Institution of Mechanical Engineers
36 Evidence of Joseph Locke, *Evidence Taken Before a Committee of the House of Commons on the Newcastle & Carlisle Railway Bill*, p158
37 Devey, J, pp40–41
38 Austin, A, p17
39 Letter, Joseph Locke to Robert Stephenson, 25 November 1825, Institution of Mechanical Engineers
40 Evidence of Joseph Locke, *Evidence Taken Before a Committee of the House of Commons on the Newcastle & Carlisle Railway Bill*, p147
41 *Proc. ICE*, XX (1861), p142: '. . . a position which he continued to fill until the completion of the line.' Evidence, *House of Commons Committee, London & Brighton Railway Bill* (London: Hansard & Son, 25 April 1836), p396, 'In the Liverpool & Manchester, where I was concerned for the whole time of its execution'. Evidence of Joseph Locke, *Report of the Commissioners Appointed to Inquire into the Application of Iron to Railway Structures*, p340: 'The resident engineer from 1826–30'.
42 Letter, Joseph Locke to Robert Stephenson, 28 February 1827, Institution of Mechanical Engineers
43 'A bound collection of newspaper cuttings relating to George & Robert Stephenson 1848–81', *Gateshead Observer*, 6 December 1851, Newcastle upon Tyne Central Library. Francis' 'whitewash' of Hudson is straight forward (Francis, J, II, pp200–27): concerning George Stephenson, the author faithfully adheres to the tales told by the subject during after-dinner speeches. As a witness before Parliamentary Select Committees, George Stephenson's evidence sometimes provoked incredulity; but with well-disposed audiences at social events, the power of his personality willed people to believe in him. To publish a contradiction of these statements would taint the Stephenson image. Therefore during his life-time, authors condoned the mythology for Robert Stephenson's sake. At times even Francis gives facts which contradict some of the fiction — if the reader is alert to them.
44 Francis, J, I, p234
45 Vignoles, O J, *Life of Charles Blacker Vignoles* (London: Longman, 1859), p110
46 Vignoles, O J, p110
47 Letter, Joseph Locke to William Roscoe, 21 March 1827, Roscoe Manuscripts, Liverpool Central Library
48 Bailey, W H, 'A new chapter in the history of the Manchester & Liverpool Railway', *Transactions of the Manchester Association of Engineers* (1889), pp23–29
49 Francis, J, I, p132–33
50 Evidence of George Leather, *Proceedings of the Committee of the House of Commons on the Liverpool & Manchester Railway Bill, Sessions 1825* (London: Thomas Davison, 1825), pp421–34
51 Vignoles, O J, 'Letter, C B Vignoles to Edward Riddle 14 January 1827', pp116–17 (also quoted in full in *Railway World*, 40 (May 1980), p238)
52 Letter, Joseph Locke to Robert Stephenson, 28 February 1827, Institution of Mechanical Engineers
53 Snell, S, *A Story of Railway Pioneers* (London: 1921), pp92–95
54 Evidence of Joseph Locke, 25 April 1836, *House of Commons Committee on the London & Brighton Railway Bill* (London: Hansard & Son, 1836), pp409–13
55 Letter, George Stephenson to Robert Stephenson, 23 February 1827, Liverpool Central Library, ref. 385 STE/11; Simmon, J, *Journal of Transport History* (September 1971), pp108–15
56 *Liverpool & Manchester Railway Company Board of Directors Minute Book*, Public Record Office, RAIL 371/1. It has wrongly been assumed that Jesse Hartley designed the Sankey Viaduct (Thomas, R H G, *The Liverpool & Manchester Railway* (London: Batsford, 1980), p44). Contemporary records suggest that Hartley was employed in a critical capacity. On 28 April 1828, he was asked to report on the Sankey drawings and specifications for the piling; that he continued to be critical is evident from a defence report, written by Joseph Locke on 7 July 1832 and signed with the initials GS (still in Locke's hand), held in the Institution of Mechanical Engineers. Haworth, V, p29; Jarvis, A, 'James Cropper, Liverpool Docks and the Liverpool & Manchester Railway', *Journal of Transport*

History (in press). All Liverpool & Manchester Railway bridge design remained Joseph Locke's responsibility. On 12 January 1829, 'The Treasurer produced . . . a paper signed by Joseph Locke being the specification of bridges remaining to be built on the line of Railway . . . the Document being required by Mr Telford' — there remained two distinct characteristic designs: those of Locke, with round arches and splayed piers, and those of Robert Stephenson, with emphatic rustication radiating from the arch to the balustrade and built after his return. On 27 March 1829, Robert Stephenson stated (*Evidence Taken Before a Committee of the House of Commons on the Newcastle & Carlisle Railway Bill*, p128) that he spent most of his time during the last eighteen months in Liverpool working on the line.

57 Francis, J, II, p150

58 Paine, E M S, *The Two James and the Two Stephensons* (London: George Phipps, 1861), pp37, 40, 43. Whereas the letters of Edward Pease and William James written between 1821 and 1823 are extremely enthusiastic about the locomotive, George Stephenson by contrast writes in a pessimistic tone and sings the praises of stationary engines at the expense of locomotives. On the Stockton & Darlington Railway he was willing to accommodate the resolutions of a general meeting to have 'as little machinery as possible' and to act 'with economy' (Stockton & Darlington Railway Minute Letters 28 July 1821 and 1 August 1821, Public Record Office, RAIL 667/30). Certainly it was William James who changed the directors' minds and inserted the additional clause for locomotives and passengers in the second Stockton & Darlington Railway Bill. A slightly disgruntled George Stephenson wrote to the locomotive advocate James on 18 December 1822: 'I would be obliged to you if you could return the Darlington Railway Act of Parliament with your alterations and remarks upon it as I hope by this time you have got everything therein properly arranged as the Darlington people wishes to see it' (Liverpool Central Library, ref. 385 JAM 1/5/6).

59 Paine, E M S, 'Letter, Lord Redesdale to William James, 16 Sept 1822', p27

60 Paine, E M S, p37

61 Trevithick, F, I, pp210, 271–76, 367; II, pp212, 217: ' . . . 9 steam engines one of which was a locomotive left 1 September 1814, Portsmouth for Lima, cost £6838.' In 1815 Richard Trevithick commissioned John Rastrick to build the first screw propeller engine with a multitubular boiler for a boat (p352). Evidence of John Rastrick, *Report of the Commissioners Appointed to Inquire into the Application of Iron to Railway Structures*, p286; Evidence of John Rastrick, *Proceedings of the Committee of the House of Commons on the Liverpool & Manchester Railway Bill, Sessions 1825*, p149: ' . . . I made one for Mr Trevithick . . . this was exhibited in London . . . I did not see it myself. A circular Railroad was laid down . . . '.

62 Trevithick, F, I, pp192–98, 207; Trevithick engine, Manufactured by Rastrick No. 14, built to be modified as a locomotive, held at the Science Museum; Trevithick visiting card, *Catch-Me-Who-Can*, 1808

63 Evidence of John Rastrick, *Proceedings of the Committee of the House of Commons on the Liverpool & Manchester Railway Bill, Sessions 1825*, pp148–92

64 Rastrick, J, 'Memoir', *Proc. ICE*, XVI (1857), p129

65 Evidence of John Rastrick, 25 November 1847, *Report of the Commissioners Appointed to Inquire into the Application of Iron to Railway Structures*, pp285–91; Collins, P (ed), *Stourbridge and its Historic Locomotives* (Dudley Leisure Services, 1989)

66 'John Rastrick', *The Dictionary of National Biography*

67 *Report of the Commissioners Appointed to Inquire into the Application of Iron to Railway Structures*, pp286–89, appendix no. 3, drawings 5–8

68 Rastrick, J, 'Memoir', *Proc. ICE*, XVI (1857), pp128–29

69 For example the Ouse Viaduct at Balcombe, Sussex.

70 *Proc. ICE*, XVI (1857), p133

71 Devey, J, p39

72 *Proc. ICE*, XIX (1860), p2

73 *Proc. ICE*, XIX (1860), p176: ' . . . the inventor and first constructor of tubular plate-iron bridges.'

74 *Proc. ICE*, XIX (1860), p2: 'His early years were devoted to the improvement and

construction of the Locomotive Engine and to him we owe the type of these machines'; *Railway Post Office Directory 1848*: 'Robert Stephenson'

75 Stephenson, R and Locke, J, *Observations on the Comparative Merits of Locomotives and Fixed Engines, as Applied to Railways etc.* (Liverpool: Wales and Baines, 1830), pp60–61

76 Wood, N, *A Practical Treatise on Rail-roads and Interior Communication in General* (London: Knight and Lacey, 1825), pp273–75, 293

77 Smiles, S, pp143–44

78 Robert Stephenson & Co. Locomotive Drawings, executed during Robert Stephenson's lifetime: no. 1, held at the Science Museum; Warren, J G H, p114

79 Dendy Marshall, C F, *A History of British Railways Down to the Year 1830* (London: Oxford University Press, 1938), p152, plate 75. George Stephenson revealed his preference for the 1815/1816 Stephenson/Dodds/ Losh Patent Locomotive Nos 3887: 4067, by providing an illustration of it without blast and with chains and steam springs in a widely distributed pamphlet issued in conjunction with his business partner, Michael Longridge, between 1824 and 1827.

80 *Robert Stephenson & Co. Minute Book*, Science Museum; Warren, J G H, p62. Concerning a patent on the improvements: 'the care of this subject is committed to Edward Pease'. Described as 'a man who could see a hundred years ahead' (Smiles, S, p150), Pease became sceptical of George Stephenson's image of intuitive ability.

81 Wood, N, p151: 'many plans have been devised to obviate the use of this chain, but nothing superior has yet been devised.'

82 Smiles, S, p487

83 Letter, Robert Stephenson to George Stephenson, 8 March 1824, Institution of Civil Engineers

84 Letter, Robert Stephenson to his step-mother Betty Stephenson, Liverpool, (June) 1824, Science Museum Library, MS1151/2. Smiles knew that Robert designed the Stockton & Darlington Railway locomotive no. 1, initially called *Active* and only later *Locomotion* by the Company — see Jarvis, A, 'An attempt at a bibliography of Samuel Smiles', *Industrial Archaeology Review*, 13 (spring 1992), p164. Because of locomotive design inhibitions imposed on him by his father, Robert anticipated how much he would be missed and consequently expected a free hand on his return — see Warren, J G H, 'Letter Edward Pease to Robert Stephenson 9 Apr 1827', *A Century of Locomotive Building by Robert Stephenson & Company*, p68: ' . . . thy father's engineering has suffered very much from thy absence.' Robert Stephenson did not take the decision lightly to sign a three-year contract with the Colombian Mining Association — see Letters, Robert Stephenson to his stepmother Betty, 4 June 1824, Science Museum Library, MS1151/1: 'This week in London has been one of the most miserable ones I have ever had in my short experience . . . Glad would I have been to . . . help in the . . . undertaking at Liverpool but I do not even now despair of taking the Chief part of his [father's] engagements on myself in a year or two.' MS1151/2, June (undated) 1824: ' . . . all is meant right.' He expresses a hope that a parcel had been received ' . . . it contained some plans'. He was obviously ensuring the completion of all design work for orders. MS1151/3, 18 June 1824: 'I have directed Messrs Herring, Graham and Powles to pay £300 per annum' to his father for the works. To give away three-fifths of his salary was a measure of his responsibility.

85 'Obituary [James Kennedy]', *Proc. IME*, 37, p532; Letter, George Stephenson to Michael Longridge, 8 August 1824, Institution of Mechanical Engineers; Gooch, T L, Diary 7 October, 14 November, 22 December 1832, Institution of Civil Engineers. Letter, Robert Stephenson to George Stephenson, 18 November 1832, Science Museum: 'If Kennedy had not obtained a great deal of information from us here, we should have stood much higher as Locomotive Engine Makers than we do now — Bury never would have made an Engine.'

86 Warren, J G H, pp118–20. A description of the first four Stockton & Darlington Railway locomotives by visiting Prussian engineers in early 1827 makes no mention of any blast pipe, whereas the blast was incorporated on the Killingworth & Hetton locomotives by Robert Stephenson in 1820–1822 (Wood, N, plate V) and on the two Springwell locomotives by Joseph Locke in 1826 (no. 1

preserved by Newcastle City Council), using a single pipe from both cylinders. In 1828 Robert Stephenson introduced twin blast pipes, one from each cylinder (Robert Stephenson & Co. drawing no. 2, held at the Science Museum); Warren, J G H, p144: the Stockton & Darlington Railway *Locomotion no. 1* was clearly modified by Robert Stephenson after 1828 according to his new blast design policy.

87 Stephenson, R and Locke, J, p4, paragraph 2
88 Stephenson, R and Locke, J, p7 paragraph 1, p6 paragraph 3
89 Stephenson, R and Locke, J, p7 paragraph 1, lines 13–14
90 Wood, N, p295
91 Tomlinson, W W, *North Eastern Railway* (Newton Abbot, 1967 — first published 1914), p142
92 Evidence of Nicholas Wood, *Proceedings of the Committee of the House of Commons on the Liverpool & Manchester Railway Bill, Sessions 1825*; Smiles, S, p500; Wood, N, p275
93 Warren, J G H, p118. The Prussian engineers visited the Stockton & Darlington Railway early in 1827: the locomotive described with the return flue was definitely one of the first four manufactured at Robert Stephenson & Co. and not to be confused with Timothy Hackworth's *Royal George* which was reconstructed from Robert Wilson's *Chittaprat* later in the year.
94 Rastrick, J, Note Book 21 January 1829, Rastrick Collection, Stirling Library, London University, MS155 IV; Warren, J G H, p122
95 Letter, George Stephenson to Robert Stephenson, 23 February 1827, Liverpool Central Library, ref. 385 STE/11
96 Devey, J, p79
97 Evidence of Joseph Locke, *Evidence Taken Before a Committee of the House of Commons on the Newcastle & Carlisle Railway Bill*, p158; Haworth, V, p9
98 *Robert Stephenson & Co. Ledger*, 30 June 1826, pp20–33, Science Museum: Springwell & Canterbury Engines
99 Stephenson, R and Locke, J, p22, paragraph 3
100 *Proc. ICE*, XX (1861), pp1, 142
101 *Proc. ICE*, XX (1861), p143. On the Liverpool & Manchester Railway, George Stephenson had to submit and allow locomotives to work the inclines (Stephenson, R and Locke, J, p21).
102 Letter, George Stephenson to Robert Stephenson, 23 February 1827, Liverpool Central Library, ref. 385 STE/11
103 Letter, Robert Stephenson to William James, 14 October 1822, Liverpool Central Library, ref. 385 JAM 1/6/4
104 Letter, Robert Stephenson to William James, 8 December 1822, Liverpool Central Libary, ref. 385 JAM 1/6/5
105 Jeaffreson, J C, I, p113
106 *Proc. ICE*, XIX (1860), p127
107 *Robert Stephenson & Co. Ledger*, Science Museum; *Liverpool & Manchester Railway Company Board of Directors Minute Book,* 20 April 1829, Public Record Office, RAIL 371/1
108 Letter, George Stephenson to Timothy Hackworth, 25 July 1828, Science Museum: '. . . but I never considered it [the horse driven dandy-cart] ought to be tried at Darlington, as I *then* considered the locomotive a better thing'.
109 *Liverpool & Manchester Railway Company Board of Directors Minute Book*; Warren, J G H, p165
110 Photograph of the manuscript, held at the Science Museum; Warren, J G H, pp166–70
111 Smiles, S, p144
112 The *Agenoria* 1828–1829, National Railway Collection; Rastrick, J, 'Memoir', *Proc. ICE*, XVI (1857), p130; 'John Rastrick', *The Dictionary of National Biography*; Collins, P (ed), pp30–47; Robert Stephenson & Co., drawings, nos 2–7, Science Museum; Warren, J G H, pp140–59
113 Jeaffreson, J C, I, p105; *Proc. ICE*, XIX (1860), p177
114 *Proc. ICE*, XIX (1860), p131: Letter, Robert Stephenson to Michael Longridge, 1 January 1828; Jeaffreson, J C, I, p115
115 *Proc. ICE*, XVI (1857), p23
116 Stephenson, R and Locke, J, p5 paragraph 3, lines 5–8 and p6 paragraph 1
117 Stephenson, R and Locke, J, p6 paragraph 2, lines 5–7 and p14 paragraph 3
118 Gurney, G, *Account of the Invention of the Steam Blast* (printed 1859)
119 Reed, B, *150 Years of British Steam Locomotives* (Newton Abbot: David & Charles, 1975), p15

120 Reed, B, p14. Whereas the author recognised that George Stephenson did not contribute one component to what ultimately became the locomotive prototype, he wrongly thought that George Stephenson built locomotives between 1815–1825. George Stephenson did not 'urge' the locomotive's adoption, as his actions and letters to W James testify (Liverpool Central Library, James collection) and Robert Stephenson was in charge of engine construction at Killingworth 1819–1822 and thereafter at Robert Stephenson & Co. with James Kennedy succeeding him 1824–1825.

121 Rastrick, J, Note Book 21 January 1829; Warren, J G H, p122

122 Walker, J, *Liverpool & Manchester Railway, Report to the Directors on the Comparative Merits of Locomotive & Fixed Engines as a Moving Power* (printed 1829), p21

123 Devey, J, p82. The idea of the multitubular boiler was not new. Richard Trevithick, patents no. 2559, 24 March 1802, and no. 3922, 6 June 1815; Trevithick, F, I, pp104, 136, 142, 352–85; Seguin & Compagnie, Patent, Ministère du Commerce & des Manufactures, 22 February 1828; Warren, J G H, pp135–39, 222

124 *Liverpool & Manchester Railway Company Board of Directors Minute Book*, 24 September 1832, Public Record Office, RAIL 371/2

125 Stephenson, R and Locke, J, p11 paragraph 1 and p23 paragraphs 2–3

126 Robert Stephenson & Co. drawings, no. 2, Science Museum; Warren, J G H, p142; Science Museum Library, MS1149; *Liverpool & Manchester Railway Company Board of Directors Minute Book*, 7 January 1828, Public Record Office, RAIL 371/1

127 Robert Stephenson & Co. drawings, no. 2A, Science Museum; Warren, J G H, p144; Stephenson, R and Locke, J, pp18–19

128 Collins, P (ed), p35: John Rastrick adopted two design features introduced by Robert Stephenson in January 1828 — the steel leaf spring and the bar frame. Warren, J G H, pp145–47, sketch and notes of *Lancashire Witch* observed working 1828, by the French engineers Coste & Perdonnet.

129 Rastrick, J, Note Book 16 January 1829

130 Walker, J, p21; Rastrick J U, *Liverpool & Manchester Railway, Report to the Directors on the Comparative Merits of Loco-motive and Fixed Engines as a Moving Power* (printed 1829)

131 Walker, J, p35; Warren, J G H, pp171–72

132 Paine, E M S, p27

133 Jeaffreson, J C, I, p124

134 Jeaffreson, J C, I, p123

135 *Liverpool & Manchester Railway Company Board of Directors Minute Book*, Public Record Office, RAIL 371/1

136 Smiles, S, p259

137 Stephenson, R and Locke, J, p6, paragraphs 1, 6

138 Stephenson, R and Locke, J, pp82–83

139 Warren, J G H, p188; Francis, J, I, p127; Jeaffreson, J C, I, p124–25

140 Francis, J, I, pp125–26

141 Francis, J, I, p57; Evidence of George Stephenson, *Proceedings of the Committee of the House of Commons on the Liverpool & Manchester Railway Bill, Sessions 1825*

142 Wood, N, pp290–91; *Quarterly Review*, 31 (1825), p362; Francis, J, I, pp102–4

143 'John Rastrick', *The Dictionary of National Biography*; Collins, P (ed), pp30–40; Trevithick, F, I, p352; Letter, R Trevithick to Hazeldine, Rastrick & Co., 30 November 1815, order for a screw-propeller engine with multitubular boiler; Trevithick, R, patent no. 3922, 6 June 1815, pp364–82 — this engine and boiler was constructed by Rastrick (pp366–67); his experience arguably exceeded that of any other engineer practising in 1829. Loree, L F, 'The four locomotives imported into America in 1829 by the Delaware & Hudson Railway Company', *Transactions of the Newcomen Society*, 5 (1924/5), pp64–72

144 Rastrick, J, 'Memoir', *Proc. ICE*, XVI (1857), p131; *Liverpool & Manchester Railway Company Board of Directors Minute Book*, 7 September 1829, Public Record Office; Warren, J G H, p173

145 Rastrick, J, Note Book 21 January 1829; Warren, J G H, pp116–17, 128

146 Warren, J G H, p119: Prussians report 'the moving parts get out of repair'.

147 Trevithick/Rastrick Engine no. 14, held at the Science Museum; Trevithick, F, II, pp18–21, 52–56, 86–87, 151, 195–97, 204–14. On 1 September 1814 nine Trevithick/Rastrick Engines left Portsmouth for Lima, one of which was a locomotive named *Sans-pareil* (pp204, 217).

148 Trevithick, R, patent no. 2599, 24 March

1802; Trevithick, F, I, pp128–145

149 Warren, J G H, pp178–79, 192, 197, 205–9

150 Smiles, S, Robert Stephenson narrative, p503

151 Warren, J G H, p209

152 See note 74. Rastrick, J, Rainhill Note Book, Science Museum; Warren, J G H, pp140–407

153 Devey, J, p91

154 Devey, J, p92

155 Devey, J, p106; *Proc. ICE*, XIX (1860), p2; Francis J, I, p126

156 Letter, James Mills to Thomas Telford, 15 December 1828, and Telford Reports, held in the Institution of Civil Engineers; Rolt, L T C, pp152–53

157 Devey, J, pp98–100

158 Rolt, L T C, p153

159 Devey, J, pp87, 122; Rolt, L T C, p153; Haworth, V, p17

160 Public Record Office, RAIL 667/30; Rolt, L T C, p78

161 Paine, E M S, p47; Public Record Office, RAIL 667/30, 17 January and 17 March 1826

162 Evidence of John Dixon, *Evidence Taken Before a Committee of the House of Commons on the Newcastle & Carlisle Railway Bill*, p66

163 Francis, J, I, p234; *Proc. ICE*, XX (1861), pp3, 145

164 Evidence of Joseph Locke, *Evidence Taken Before a Committee of the House of Commons on the Newcastle & Carlisle Railway Bill*, p158; Public Record Office, Stockton & Darlington Railway, 667/274 and 667/278; Devey, J, p122

165 Jeaffreson, J C, I, p153

166 Rolt, L T C, p154

167 Leeds & Hull Railway via Selby, surveyed Locke 1825, Leeds & Selby Act 29 May 1830, Engineer James Walker; Newcastle & Carlisle Railway, surveyed Locke 1825, Act 22 May 1829, Engineer Francis Giles; Sheffield & Manchester Railway via Stockport, surveyed Locke 1829, Act 5 May 1837, Engineer C B Vignoles, passed back to Locke 1838; Manchester & Leeds Railway, surveyed Locke 1830, Bill thrown out, resubmitted, surveyed by Francis Whishaw, Act passed 14 July 1836; Limerick to Waterford, Dublin to Kingston, surveyed Locke 1831/2, railways passed to C B Vignoles; London & Birmingham Railway, surveyed Robert Stephenson 1830, 1831 and 1832, Bill thrown out 1832, Act passed May 1833, Robert Stephenson engineer-in-chief.

168 Jeaffreson, J C, I, p178

169 Rolt, L T C, p225

170 Jeaffreson, J C, I, pp167, 181

171 Documents relating to the formation of George Stephenson & Co., Darlington Public Library; Warren, J G H, pp63–64

172 Letter, Robert Stephenson to Thomas Richardson, 17 December 1829; Jeaffreson, J C, I, p152

173 John Rastrick Collection, Stirling Library, London University; Webster, N W, *Britain's First Trunk Railway* (Bath: Adams & Dart, 1972), pp23–25

174 Letter, Joseph Locke to George Stephenson, 29 December 1832, Chesterfield Public Library, ref. SI 28D

175 Mackenzie Collection, William Mackenzie's Letter Book, Institution of Civil Engineers

176 Evidence of Joseph Locke, 13 March 1837, *Minutes of Evidence, House of Commons Committee, London & Brighton Railway Bill* (London: Leighton & Murray, 1837); Public Record Office, RAIL 220/43 plans & sections parts I & II by J Locke and J Rastrick: 220/34 plans & sections signed by J Rastrick. Rastrick continued to suport Locke, nominating him as a Fellow of the Royal Society and in 1837 encouraging the Glasgow, Paisley & Greenock Railway Board to employ the aspiring young man as their engineer (Scottish Record Office, GPG/1/1 Minute Book 1835–38, p83).

177 Devey, J, p97

178 Devey J, p103; Rolt, L T C, pp211–13; Public Record Office, RAIL 220/1, 18 Sept 1833, 25 Sept 1833, 22 Oct 1833; RAIL 220/35 plans for bridges signed Joseph Locke; RAIL 220/20–24 agreements with contracts and specifications. The first two are with John Stephenson.

179 Haworth, V, pp4–10; Dendy Marshall, C F, p152, fig. 75

180 Letter, Edward Pease to George Stephenson, 9 April 1834, Chesterfield Public Library, ref. SI 29 C; *Proc. ICE*, XVI (1857), p293–94; Devey, J, p111; 'Joseph Locke', *The Dictionary of National Biography*; Public Record Office, RAIL 220/1, 12 and 14 May 1835, RAIL 384/111 & 118 — Locke's rails.

181 Public Record Office, RAIL 220/1, 16 September 1833; Trevithick, F, I, p213. Robert Stephenson could have intervened and

organised his father's southern section himself: that he chose not to speaks for itself.

182 *Proc. ICE*, XX (1861), p2

183 Devey, J, p149

184 *Proc. ICE*, XI (1852), p467

185 *Proc. ICE*, XX (1861), p146

186 Devey, J, p111

187 Sheffield & Manchester Railway: due to Charles Blacker Vignoles' problems, particularly at Woodhead Tunnel and with logistics, Joseph Locke became engineer-in-chief in November 1839. *Proc. ICE*, XX (1861), p3: Locke 'encountered and overcame engineering difficulties with great skill' on the Sheffield & Manchester Railway; Francis (Francis, J, I, p234) attributes the magnificent viaducts at Dinting Vale and Etherow and the tunnel to Locke. The Company Minute Book reveals (24 April 1839) that Vignoles intended a stone viaduct at Dinting. Locke designed a wooden structure. Contrary to various assumptions, he did not adopt any of Vignoles' designs. London & Southampton Railway: Francis, J, I, p231: 'Mr Giles resigned . . . the services of Mr Locke were procured, a complete plan showing the work was drawn out . . . there was a thorough revision . . . '. Devey, J, p117; Rolt, L T C, p216. Again, Locke found it necessary to undo the engineering design and begin again, yet was obliged to adhere to the route passed by Parliament. A recent tendency to give joint credit to Vignoles and Locke, and to Francis Giles and Locke for these railways seems unjust. Even the Great Western Company had doubts about their engineer, I K Brunel, whose slow progress was extremely costly: the Board Minutes of December 1838 show that only the Chairman's vote stopped the move to recruit Locke.

188 Jeaffreson, J C, I, p252

189 Gray, T, *Observations on a General Iron Railway* (printed 1820); James, W, *Advantages of Direct Inland Communication by Line of Engine Railroad* (printed 1820 and 1823); Francis, J, I, pp73, 80–87; Paine, E M S, pp39–43

190 Devey, J, p110; Haworth, V, p19

191 Stephenson, R, Diary 26 September 1834: G P Bidder entered Robert Stephenson's Office. Grundy, F, *Pictures of the Past* (Griffith and Farrar, 1879), pp114–15: in 1837 Bidder 'was at that time and continued to be until their deaths, principal manager and partner of George Stephenson & Son' (*Boyle's Court Guide* and *Listed Postal Directory* until 1842, thereafter under Civil Engineers). There is no evidence of a formal business partnership with Robert Stephenson. Page 154: 'George Bidder was one of the pleasantest fellows going . . . and one of the shrewdest.' Circumstantial evidence suggests that during the Grand Junction debacle, which led to George Stephenson's eventual resignation, Robert Stephenson needed a go-between to relieve himself of the pressures of his father's overpowering personality and to distance himself from George Stephenson's business activities (Haworth, V, pp18–20). Bidder seems to have been willing and able to fill this role, both as an engineer and as a friend. As Robert Stephenson had severed his ties with George Stephenson & Son, his workforce was employed by the London & Birmingham Railway Company. On 19 March 1835 Bidder obtained permission from the Railway to leave, his first railway project with George Stephenson being the London & Blackwall. Bidder played his role to perfection, finding Old George, as he was affectionately known, secretaries, etc. (Grundy, F, pp113–24) and easing the tension between father and son. For this essential service he was eventually rewarded with a third of Robert Stephenson' estate. Jeaffreson, J C, I, p253; Robert Stephenson's Will — Somerset House; Death Duty Registers, Public Record Office, Chancery Lane, London; Science Museum Library, MS2033.

192 Thomas Gooch Memoirs, manuscript held in Institution of Civil Engineers. Thomas Gooch was a relative of Michael Longridge (director of George Stephenson & Son and of Robert Stephenson & Co.) Unlike his brothers Daniel and John, who chose to break away from those establishments, Thomas remained a loyal henchman of George Stephenson: his fate, therefore, became bound up with that of his employer.

193 Letter, Joseph Locke to George Stephenson, 30 June 1832, Chesterfield Public Library, ref. S129B: Locke prepared to protect William Allcard's interests. Haworth, V, pp17–18; Letter, Joseph Locke to Robert

Stephenson, 28 February 1827, Institution of Mechanical Engineers; Letter, Michael Longridge to Robert Stephenson, written between 2 November 1825 and 16 July 1826, Darlington Public Library: Steel shot himself in the George Stephenson & Son/Robert Stephenson & Co. office.

194 Thomas Gooch Memoirs, Institution of Civil Engineers: 'This step caused me much anxious thought before I decided in its favour.'

195 Whishaw, F, 'Memoir', *Proc. ICE*, XVI (1857), pp143–50

196 Roscoe, T, *The London & Birmingham Railway* (London: Charles Tilt, 1838), p96. Typical Robert Stephenson masonry arch designs on the Manchester & Leeds compare with the London & Birmingham Railway. Also his bow-string girder type, pp1, 60. It was Robert Stephenson's habit to allow his associates and employees the whim of applying peripheral detail to basic structural designs (Grundy, F, pp114–15). On the Manchester & Leeds Railway, two of Robert's bow-string girders have Gothic tracery and turrets added by either Gooch or George Stephenson: the larger bow-string at Whiteley Arches, Charlestown is devoid of decoration—as it left the drawing board.

197 Thomas Gooch Memoirs, Institution of Civil Engineers: the Manchester & Leeds Railway was divided into twenty-four districts with separate contracts, 'apart from two they were satisfactorily wound up and settled by myself and these two were readily adjusted by reference to Mr Robert Stephenson as Arbiter.'

198 British Rail Archives: 16732 (BARCRO NEG 3483) plan & transverse section drawing no. IV, tie bars drawing no. V, longitudinal section drawing no. 1, 105775 longitudinal section marked LMSR Hunts Bank & British Railways Board 20 May 1982

199 Letter, George Stephenson to Thomas Gooch, 31 October 1841, Institution of Mechanical Engineers

200 Letter, George Stephenson to Thomas Gooch, 4 November 1841, Institution of Mechanical Engineers

201 Letter, George Stephenson to Thomas Gooch, 31 October 1841, Institution of Mechanical Engineers

202 Thomas Gooch Journals and Memoirs, Institution of Civil Engineers. Sometimes what is stated in the contemporary daily journals is contradicted in the memoirs written after the deaths of Robert Stephenson and Joseph Locke. It is significant that Journal no. 3 covering the time of the false claims is missing. Gooch himself must have destroyed it because he adds a memorandum on 12 April 1826 stating the events of the next few months. Memoirs: 'From defective education, George Stephenson was not able to write his own business letter — I thus became his amanuensis, writing all his letters for him . . . I was in fact his sole draughtsman and secretary from the commencement of the works of the Liverpool & Manchester Railway in 1826 until April 1829 . . . '. Numerous letters and reports signed by George Stephenson have survived. None is in Gooch's distinctive handwriting. Most are written by Locke, who was George Stephenson's paid clerk and who executed the plans and bridge designs of the Liverpool & Manchester Railway, as independent records reveal. Some letters are in William Allcard's hand. In his Memoir, Thomas Gooch does not mention John Stephenson's employment ensuring the success of the Summit Tunnel's construction.

203 Institution of Civil Engineers, Robert Stephenson, *Railway Newspaper Cuttings*, last page, testimonial; Public Record Office, RAIL 384/194 & 195, London & Birmingham Railway extension, 1844

204 Jeaffreson, J C, I, pp240–42

205 Jeaffreson, J C, I, p243

206 Rolt, L T C, pp265–75; Jeaffreson, J C, I, p251; Haworth, V, pp16, 19–20

207 Locke, J, *The London & Glasgow Railway Through Lancashire* (printed 1836)

208 Webster, N W, p139

209 Locke, J, *The London & Glasgow Railway Through Lancashire*

210 Devey, J, p141

211 Scottish Record Office, BR/CAL4/69/7, p53; Locke wrote, 1829–1830: 'previous railways had not been constructed with due regard to the best sectional line' (Stephenson, R and Locke, J). Because of his vast surveying experience 1825–1830, Locke became the unrivalled master of assessing the lie of the land, able to select the best route over difficult terrain.

212 Devey, J, pp124–31; Snell, S, pp85–87, 93

213 Scottish Record Office, BR/CAL1/100, p73: Campbell, D, to Locke, J: 'You recommended Mr Stephenson and no tenders were taken from other parties.'
214 Mackenzie, W, 'Memoir', *Proc. ICE*, XI (1852), p104
215 Mackenzie Collection, William Mackenzie Diary, 20 October 1847, Institution of Civil Engineers
216 Scottish Record Office, BR/CAL4/74/22. Letter, Joseph Locke to J J Hope Johnstone, 18 August 1847
217 Scottish Record Office, BR/CAL4/74/46. Letter, John Stephenson to Captain Goddington, 15 December 1847
218 Day, J, *A Practical Treatise on the Construction and Formation of Railways* (printed 1839 and 1848)
219 Snell, S, p93
220 Scottish Record Office, BR/CAL4/74/2, 27 February and 7 April 1846 — documents relating to the education of labourers to be paid for by Stephenson & Co: '... there shall be one or two scripture teachers'.
221 Death Duty Registers, John Stephenson, Public Record Office, Chancery Lane, London. IR26/1819 folios 131, 132. The winding up of his estate took over two years: the total after taxes was £90,672. Mackenzie took on the responsibility to complete the Caledonian Railway. Scottish Record Office, BR/CAL4/74/56
222 Rolt, L T C, p48
223 Roscoe, T, p69
224 *Newcastle Chronicle,* 2 August 1850, Newcastle upon Tyne Central Library. Public Dinner to Robert Stephenson, speech by Scott Russell.
225 Hartree Papers 1119 M/E 11, Robert Stephenson Narrative Manuscript, pp12–13, Devon County Record Office
226 *The Engineer*, I (1883), p217
227 Letter, Robert Stephenson to Henry Booth, 3 August 1829, photographs of original manuscript held at the Science Museum; Warren, J G H, p177
228 Letter, Robert Stephenson to Henry Booth, 5 September 1829, photographs of original manuscript held at Science Museum; Warren, J G H, p181
229 *Proc. ICE*, XVI (1857), p23
230 Jeaffreson, J C, I, p115: Letter, Robert Stephenson to Michael Longridge, 1 January 1828
231 Evidence of Joseph Locke, *Report of the Gauge Commissioners* (London: Harrison, 1846), p23; Webster, N W, p131
232 'Joseph Locke', *The Dictionary of National Biography*; Trevithick, F, I, pp213–14. A quotation of Joseph Locke's report of 31 December 1839, concerning his intentions with regard to the Crewe Type locomotive. It would appear that Locke knew Francis Trevithick well and discussed this report with him. However William Buddicom was first appointed by Locke as Locomotive Superintendent to the Grand Junction Railway in 1839 and fulfilled Locke's intentions. Because he had already constructed Locke's design for the winding engines at the Lime Street Tunnel, Buddicom's abilities were known to the engineer-in-chief. Previously employed at Robert Stephenson & Co. from 1832, Alexander Allan was also selected by Locke to work under Buddicom as 'foreman of the workshops' with a salary of £250 a year. After Allan left under a cloud in 1853, he made false claims with regard to the Crewe locomotive, published in Clark, D K, *Railway Machinery* (London: Blackie & Son, 1855), p15. False claims have also been made on behalf of Buddicom; again the initiative clearly came from Locke, who within a year transferred Buddicom to Sotteville (*Proc. ICE*, XVII (1858), p144) allowing the talented mechanical engineer to establish his own company, Allcard, Buddicom & Co. Francis Trevithick, who succeeded Buddicom as Locomotive Superintendent to the Grand Junction Railway, stated that for the next seventeen years (1840–1856) he 'acted on the advice of Locke and the initial 1839 report, though of necessity the strict letter had to be varied with the change of time and circumstance'. Papers of George Neumann (favourite pupil of Locke), Science Museum Library, folder 3 1/21. Design of machinery to work the trains in the new tunnel (Lime Street) signed Joseph Locke 5 March 1836. It is ironic that the only surviving engine designs signed by Locke are of stationary engines.
233 Haworth, V, p16. In claiming credit for his son's achievements, George Stephenson set an unacceptable trend and a few of his associates

followed suit, e.g. Booth in 1829 and then the manufacturer Fairbairn and the architect Dobson in the aftermath of the Dee disaster. William Fairbairn claimed the initiative in the tubular girder (note 235, below). Edwin Clark's letters to Robert Stephenson written prior to May 1847 show this was false. Then John Dobson, one of Hudson's circus, allowed others to imply that he played a creative role in the design of Newcastle Central Station's train shed roof. After Hudson's downfall, Dobson lost many lucrative projects: ten years after the event the architect himself made priority claims, but details given show his ignorance concerning wrought-iron development in general and its application to train shed roofs in particular.

234 Conder, F, *Personal Recollections of English Engineers* (Hodder & Stroughton, 1868, reprinted London: Thomas Telford, 1983), p141: 'although designed by an assistant who was famous for his powers of calculations, it is unaccountable that the practical eye of Mr Stephenson should have been for a moment blind.' Haworth, V, p18. Even though the railway world knew that George Parker Bidder had actually designed the Dee bridge and that this truss-girder type had been introduced by him (Jeaffreson, J C, II, p48), Robert Stephenson's decision to stand trial as being responsible was accepted. It may be significant that the only prominent member of the engineering profession to be absent both from court and the succeeding commission (*The Application of Iron to Railway Structures*) was Bidder, who then suffered a nervous breakdown, and went to work for a life insurance company. There was some reticence on the part of railway companies to be officially connected with him, but Robert Stephenson attempted to ensure his involvement with the Swiss and Norwegian railways. Bidder had been wealthy, but, presumably because of the lack of railway business, now had to take out a substantial mortgage from Robert Stephenson which was only extinguished when Bidder inherited one third of the estate. Science Museum MS2033.

235 Fairbairn, W, *The Construction of the Britannia and Conway Tubular Bridges with a complete History of the progress by William Fairbairn* (London: Longman, 1849); a criticism of the book in *The Civil Engineers & Architects Journal* (August 1849), pp251–53: 'But enough is before us to warrant us in affirming that Mr Fairbairn deals unfairly both with his own fame, and with that of his colleagues in assuming a controversial tone — unfairly towards them, by endeavouring to depreciate their merits, unfairly towards himself because the attempt will re-act against himself . . . '.

236 Jeaffreson, J C, II, pp303–4. Evidence of Eaton Hodgkinson, *Report of the Commissioners Appointed to Inquire into the Application of Iron to Railway Structures*, pp115–80 and evidence of Edwin Clark, pp359–64; Clark, E, *The Britannia and Conway Tubular Bridges*, 2 vols (London: Day & Son, 1850), written with the sanction and under the immediate supervision of Robert Stephenson.

237 Evidence of Joseph Locke, *Report of the Commissioners Appointed to Inquire into the Application of Iron to Railway Structures*, p345

238 Robert Stephenson & Co. drawings, nos 12, 12A, Science Museum; Warren, J G H, pp238, 240

239 *Proc. ICE*, XIX (1860), p176

240 *Newcastle Chronicle*, see note 224

241 Jeaffreson, J C, I, p155

242 *Newcastle Chronicle*, see note 224

243 Scottish Public Record Office, RHP 47464 Tay Bridge at Perth 22 July 1847, signed Joseph Locke; Science Museum, Neumann Papers, Folder 31/2 Stationary Engine 5 March 1836, signed Joseph Locke; Science Museum, Robert Stephenson & Co. drawings, for example nos 1, 8, 14, 18A exhibit Robert Stephenson's handwriting: some have his intentions, some calculations.

244 Writers often make the mistake of interpreting personal documents such as a daily diary, a journal or a letter, in isolation, instead of comparing it with other related documents and within the known circumstantial evidence, thus giving an inflated impression of the subject. Someone employed as a draughtsman or calculator could record 'designing' a bridge or an engine but only be obeying instructions from a higher source. For instance: Institution of Civil Engineers, T Gooch's Diary 1826:

Jan 28 At Plan of Travelling Engine all day
Jan 25 Drawing Travelling Engine all day
Feb 1 Joined Locke and levelled

Feb 16 Planning arch of Tunnel for Canterbury Railway
Feb 18 At Travelling Engine Plan and the one for Canterbury
Feb 20 Back with Locke levelling

Even though Gooch admits in his Memoirs that he was working under Locke, a fully fledged mining engineer at this time, the potential for error is there. Again, from George Phipps' 'Memoir', *Proc. ICE*, XCVI (1889), p331, it may be wrongly concluded that Phipps designed the Weedon Viaduct on the London & Birmingham Railway. Robert Stephenson's 1834 Diary reveals he had done the initial drawing.

245 *Proc. ICE*, XCVI (1889), p330; *The Engineer* (1883) part I, p217; Warren, J G H, p175

246 Mackenzie Collection, William Mackenzie Diary, 13 January 1846, Institution of Civil Engineers; Clark, E, II, p482. The architect Francis Thompson was employed by Robert Stephenson in exactly the same way. He was '. . . engaged with Mr. Stephenson in preparing the designs for the masonry, and he was both instructed to complete his drawings for the foundations to establish the quantity of masonry & prepare the plans & specifications to lay before the contractors'. They were 'ready for inspection' on 17 March 1846. There is no evidence to suggest that either Tite or Thompson acted in a creative design capacity when they executed these or any other drawings of structures under or over a railway: that was the domain of the engineer-in-chief.

247 *The Gateshead Observer*, 3 August 1850. Paintings of the major railway structures in Newcastle were even exhibited prior to the passing of the Bill. The public reaction to Robert Stephenson's Dean Street Viaduct was: 'a complete bar and blot to the view up the side and deprive strangers of the pleasure of seeing the steeple of St Nicholas Church'. In April 1846 a painting of the proposed High Level Bridge '. . . executed by that distinguished artist, Mr Carmichael, was publically exhibited in Newcastle' (now in the Laing Art Gallery, Newcastle upon Tyne); House of Lords Record Office, *Manuscript Evidence in the Newcastle & Berwick Railway,* House of Lords, 4, session 1845. The Dean Street arch flanked on each side by three small arches was constructed between 1845 and 1848 when this section of the railway became fully operational. Even though Robert Stephenson defended his Dean Street Viaduct design before Parliament, in the light of his 'experience' he is not given credit for his structure in any known secondary source. Robert Stephenson kept his distance from the Hudson circus, which included Dobson. There is no evidence of any working liaison between the engineer and the architect. Nor was Dobson appointed as architect for the Central Station's facade until 1846, that is after the drawings of the Dean Street Viaduct had been circulated. Dobson did however collaborate with J W Carmichael for some watercolours of the Central Station, now in the Laing Art Gallery, Newcastle upon Tyne. *Perspectives on Railway History & Interpretation* (York: National Railway Museum, 1992). Chapter one illustrates paintings of Robert Stephenson's structures (plates 1.5, 1.8) and also of Joseph Locke's structures (plate 1.9), but fails to mention the engineers who designed them.

248 Public Record Office, High Level Bridge Contract, RAIL 772/34, p5; Jeaffreson, J C, II, p126.

249 Evidence of Joseph Locke, *Report of the Commissioners Appointed to Inquire into the Application of Iron to Railway Structures*, p341

250 Weale, J, *Supplement to the Theory, Practice and Architecture of Bridges* (London: Weale, 1850), plates XI, XII, XIV, XV, labelled 'Descriptions of plan, elevation and details of the bridge over the commercial road for the Blackwall Extension', engineer, Joseph Locke; manufacturer, Fox & Henderson: '. . . this is a very beautiful application of wrought iron . . . one of the first all wrought iron bow string girders'. Plates XVI, XVII and XVIII, labelled 'Bridge over the Thames at Richmond, on the Richmond Railway', engineer: Joseph Locke: 'Few of our modern engineers have been so successful as Mr Locke in the economical application of cast iron. Upon the Grand Junction and upon some of the Scottish railways are numerous instances of the great skill with which he applied that material . . . including three bridges over the Thames . . . '. Brees, S C, *Railway Practice. A Collection of Working Plans and Practical Details of Construction in the Public Works of the Most Celebrated Engineers* (London: John Williams,

1837), Grand Junction Railway, Joseph Locke, plate 58, details of iron bridges. Plate 61, details of proposed foot bridges. These bridges present a very light appearance, and are of a very economical principle, considering their permanency. Second edition published 1838, Grand Junction Railway, Joseph Locke. Plate LXI, details of iron bridges. Plate LXIV, details of proposed foot bridges. Although Joseph Locke was recognised by his contemporaries as a leading exponent of iron bridge structures, this fact has been generally forgotten. See also the numerous plans in the Public Record Office (Kew) and the Scottish Record Office.

251 *The Times*, 21 September 1860; *Proc. ICE*, XX (1861), p146

252 *Proc. ICE*, XIX (1860), p3

253 Brees, S C, 3rd edn (1847), plate 65. Details of Principal for centre roof at Hunts Bank Station. Engineer: Robert Stephenson. Hunts Bank was the Manchester terminal station of the Manchester & Leeds Railway. Charles Wild described how he, as resident engineer, was in charge of the construction of another Euston Truss-type roof at Chester under Robert Stephenson's direction. *Report of the Commissioners Appointed to Inquire into the Application of Iron to Railway Structures*, p350. The first design (1837–1838) is described in great detail by Roscoe, T, p161: 'Curzon Street, Birmingham . . . the finest roof in the world,' but the label Euston has been given to this truss type, the other terminus of the London & Birmingham Railway. Every third rib was supported by a pillar some of which acted as drain pipes, a hall-mark of all Robert Stephenson's train shed roofs, even the Central Station, Newcastle upon Tyne.

254 *Newcastle Chronicle* (note 224), Speech of Robert Stephenson; Jeaffreson, J C, II, p139 — Harrison also confirms his role as resident engineer for the roof structure. He did not work for John Dobson; Conder, F, p83. The architect was 'expected to prepare the façade and elevation of the terminal buildings . . . ', the design of the roof and the platform arrangements were ' . . . the nominal function of the Engineer-in-Chief'; *Proc. ICE*, XVII (1858), p449: '. . . passenger train shed design and construction is in the hands of a few engineers.'

255 Conder, F, p14

New insights from the Mackenzie collection

Mary Murphy

Posterity has not been kind to William Mackenzie. (Plate 4) In his own lifetime he was one of the foremost contractors of the early Victorian period carrying out (on his own or with partners) contracts in excess of £17 million. The Institution of Civil Engineers published a three-page obituary when he died, in itself an indication of his importance.[1] The *Liverpool Mercury* referred to him as an 'eminent railway contractor . . . [whose] whole life was spent in carrying out public works of the highest order and most lasting utility'.[2] Yet now, his name is largely unknown and surpassed in the popular consciousness by that of his junior partner, Thomas Brassey. I cannot give an authoritative reason for this phenomenon, but with the acquisition by the Institution of Civil Engineers of the archive now known as the Mackenzie collection, there exists an opportunity to try to discover how this has come about, and to make a fresh assessment of the relative importance of Mackenzie. This would allow some progress to be made towards answering the first historiographical problem addressed by the conference, namely, what governs the selection of individuals for immortality?

My usual response when questioned about the contrast between the well-known Brassey and the lesser-known Mackenzie is to refer to the patriotic and romantic imagery of the Crimean Railway, or the great adventure of the Victoria bridge over the St Lawrence River constructed for the Grand Trunk Railway of Canada. Such bold undertakings would have appealed to the Victorians and helped Brassey's name survive. Both these projects were undertaken after Mackenzie's death. A further aid to immortality must surely be a biography in the mould of A Helps' biography of Brassey,[3] which, while sadly lacking in technical detail, is certainly full of paeans of praise and anecdotes designed to show their subject to best advantage. It was not until I started the research for this paper that I realised how little detail there is in the aforementioned biography about the contracts undertaken, especially for the period of Mackenzie's lifetime. An interesting item in the Mackenzie collection is the family copy of this book with marginal notes and exclamations. There are also letters from former colleagues expressing indignation that Helps did not acknowledge the debt they felt Brassey owed to Mackenzie for his own success. There are even drafts of letters to *The Times* expressing these sentiments sent for approval, but this was 30 years after Mackenzie's death, and perhaps it was felt no useful purpose could be served by raising the ghosts of the past. Unfortunately no comparable biography was written about William Mackenzie.

The Mackenzie collection provides some remarkable insights into the work of a busy civil engineer and contractor during the first half of the nineteenth century — an age of tremendous opportunity and expansion. It provides information on the finance and organisation of his contracts, the difficulties encountered both in this country and abroad, and his working relationships with various notable civil engineers, financiers, landowners, craftsmen, businessmen, gangers and workmen.

Acquisition of the collection

This material was acquired through the generosity of the late Miss Margaret Mackenzie, great-great-niece of William Mackenzie and great-granddaughter of Edward Mackenzie, William's younger brother and partner. It is perhaps one of the most important and comprehensive collections acquired this century, containing approximately 1000 drawings, twenty diaries, various letterbooks, notebooks, letters, agreements, ledgers, contracts, tenders, specifications, insurance policies, bills, receipts, etc. Yet the Institution of Civil Engineers was completely unaware of the existence of these papers until we were first approached in 1988 and asked if we would like to view some family papers connected with civil engineering. Since the middle of the nineteenth century these papers had remained in the family's care, which may explain why Mackenzie's name faded into obscurity. If they had been accessible, studies and biographies might well have been published before now. The papers had been stored variously in office, library, attic and stables and consequently their condition varied from near perfect to irreparably damaged.

The initial assessment and preliminary listing, which revealed the tremendous scope of the material, were followed by two years of patient negotiation. Eventually we were fortunate to acquire the whole collection on condition that the material should remain together as the Mackenzie collection and be made available for research and study — conditions we were happy to satisfy.

The Institution was so impressed with the importance of the collection that a citation was presented to Miss Mackenzie, and she was made a Companion of the Institution, an honour of which she was singularly proud. Sadly, she died a few months later.

The Institution's immediate concern following the acquisition of the collection was the conservation of materials which needed treatment to ensure their preservation. Once the collection had been removed to the Institution, a comprehensive programme of conservation was initiated, starting with the drawings and progressing to notebooks, letterbooks, ledgers, diaries, letters, etc. Bindings, where required, are in the style of the original, and where feasible original bindings or nameplates have been re-used. Once conserved, the materials are catalogued and made available for consultation and research, although in the case of the more fragile material, we anticipate the need to microfilm in order to preserve the original.

William Mackenzie: life and career

The following resumé of William Mackenzie's life and career concentrates on some of his British works, leading up to the establishment of the partnership with Thomas Brassey and their tremendous expansion as contractors overseas.

William Mackenzie was born on 20 March 1794 at Marsden Chapel (near Nelson, Lancashire), the eldest son of Alexander Mackenzie who at that time was working on the Leeds and Liverpool Canal. Alexander was also a contractor, albeit on a more modest scale, the registers recording the births of his children showing him variously as labourer, canal cutter, navigator and miner. It was on the Leeds and Liverpool Canal that William Mackenzie began his career, apprenticed to Thomas Clapham, a lock carpenter. This was followed by work on Troon Harbour under John Clapham, which gave him knowledge of cranes, wagons, caissons and general plant, and methods of submarine construction.

He may have first met Thomas Telford while employed by John Cargill on the construction of Craigellachie Bridge, but it was not until 1824 that his important association with Telford began. In the meantime, from 1816 onwards, he was employed by Hugh McIntosh as agent on the Edinburgh and Glasgow Union Canal (under Hugh Baird) engaged in measuring, levelling, setting out and taking account of work on that part of the canal between Falkirk and Edinburgh. The collection includes specifications for this work.

In 1819 he married his first wife Mary Dalziel, daughter of James Dalziel of Glasgow and Rothesay, Isle of Bute. He continued to work with McIntosh on the Gloucester–Berkeley Canal until 1824, when he accepted an appointment as superintendent of works under Telford of the Mythe bridge across the Severn at Tewkesbury, his account of this bridge being published in the *Transactions of the Institution of Civil Engineers*.[4] He progressed in 1826 to the position of resident engineer under Telford on the Birmingham Canal improvements, which involved some of the greatest excavations to date in this country, especially the deep cuttings at the summit level (1826–1829) and the tunnel for the feeder from Rotten Park Reservoir. Included in the collection for this period are not only records of excavations,[5] but also specifications, drawings of bridges,[6] a gauging lock and tollhouse,[7] and a letterbook.[8] His final report to Telford with a copy of the final accounts was sent on 5 October 1830, after which he seemed to be working independently, reporting to the Commissioners and setting out his own estimates for the many branches that were required. This would have been two to four years before Telford's death.

By 1832, the work was complete and his position was terminated, although he was still acting as a mediator on behalf of Thomas Townshend (one of the contractors) in some financial disputes until 1834, and his diary of 1840 shows him visited by Townshend and again reading over Townshend's contract with the Birmingham Canal Co.

Possibly because of his early experience with canals and possibly because of Telford's influence, he was said to have had an early prejudice against railways.[9] However, when the new railways caused an increase in the demand for contractors, he must have realised that his own recent experience of tunnelling and earthworks put him in a strong position to compete for contracts. Quick to see the opportunity, he capitalised on his advantage.

His first contract was for the Great Tunnel from Edge Hill to Lime Street Station on the Liverpool & Manchester Railway under George Stephenson. There were a number of problems connected with this contract, and, in view of these and the various delays, it is perhaps remarkable that he finally completed this contract ahead of schedule.[10] Originally Longworth and Gordon McLeod were his partners in this venture but they withdrew before the work had started (because of the time limit it has been said).[11] However, Mackenzie was able to continue the contract, with Henry Haydock, a Liverpool merchant, as his surety, under the direction of William Allcard. Mackenzie's letterbook for this period[12] contains a number of letters which shed light on his work for the Liverpool & Manchester Railway and the frustrations he experienced at times.

In November 1832, Mackenzie requested the exact level of the tunnel at the Crown Street shaft before he could proceed; in January 1833, he informed Allcard of a change in stratification at the Asylum shaft, urging immediate excavation and brick arching; in February 1833 he requested that the straight line of the tunnel be marked at Chatham Street so that a further shaft could be sunk; and in May of that year he complained that his workmen were standing idle, as the width of the entrance to the tunnel mouth had not yet been fixed. It is perhaps not surprising that following Joseph Locke's report into the alignment of the tunnel Allcard resigned, although exonerated, and was replaced by John Dixon.

In August 1833 Mackenzie instructed McLeod that no implements or materials were to be lent or ordered for McLeod's portion of the work without express orders from himself, and the following month requested McLeod not to deposit any more earth or stone on the Broad Green Embankment until further orders. Possibly he had taken on McLeod as a sub-contractor, for a year later he told him he could no longer put up with his conduct and gross negligence, and intended to measure up his portion of the line and pay him off.[13]

With all the problems that occurred during the construction of the Great Tunnel it would not be surprising if he had expressed the sentiments which he so vehemently denied in a letter to Stephenson towards the end of 1833,[14] '. . . that I had been heard to say I hoped or would be glad if you would not get the appointment of Principal Engineer to the Grand Junction Railway from Warrington to Birmingham.' He continues, '. . . I deny the assertion in toto and beg leave to challenge the individual who told such a gross and infamous falsehood to you . . .'. Perhaps it is necessary to read between the lines in order to ascertain his true feelings.

During this period Mackenzie also undertook other work in the area, such as the sinking of a well at Liverpool Workhouse, the construction of embankments for the Whiston branch line, additional works at the east end of the New Tunnel at Edge Hill, retaining walls from Wavertree Lane to the New Tunnel, the enlargement of the retaining walls in the Olive Mount cutting, drains on the small tunnel from the New Tunnel mouth to the engine boilers, excavation of Cattle Market Yard, and a drain from the North Railway Tunnel to the engine well at Mr Ethes' Ropery. Yet he was still experiencing problems, and in June 1834 he wrote to Henry Booth complaining that he had been waiting several days for the short Whiston branch to be set out, and, as a consequence, his men were thrown idle and losing the benefit of the fine weather. He was sure he need not remind Booth of the number of delays experienced since the branch was commenced, and hoped Booth would make the necessary arrangements so that he might proceed to finish the work forthwith.[15]

While occupied with these works, Mackenzie was also engaged in contracts for the Grand Junction Railway. As early as March 1833, prior to the Act for the Grand Junction Railway being passed, Mackenzie was requested by Locke to give some guidance about the likely cost of works on the projected route. A few days later Mackenzie tendered for four excavation contracts between Warrington and Bitley as well as the contract for the Warrington viaduct which spanned the River Mersey and the Irwell and Mersey Canal, which he undertook successfully with James Crompton and James Dalziel (possibly his brother-in-law).

Mackenzie's younger brother Edward joined him while he was working on the Liverpool & Manchester Railway and many contracts followed over the next few years: C and J B Faviell's contracts on the Wigan and Preston, the Manchester and Salford Junction Canal, the Midland Counties Railway, the Peak Forest Canal (as consultant), etc. In May 1835 he was engaged simultaneously on the Liverpool & Manchester, the Grand Junction and the North Union Railways (Plate 5) when his tender for the North Union Railway under Charles Blacker Vignoles was accepted. A year later he was experiencing problems with this contract, and apologised for any difficulty that Hardman Earle was experiencing on his behalf. He even wondered if it would not have been better 'if the works had been allotted to some of the other parties what with interference on the works and one thing and another'. The directors took him at his word and gave notice that they would 'take their own steps of proceeding with the Yarrow contracts'.[16] However, they seem to have reconsidered their decision for later Mackenzie was completing the works, although he still had problems. Some of the ground south of the Yarrow was much harder than expected. Part of a central pier and embankment had collapsed during construction after Vignoles and John Collister had changed the design of a bridge from a single arch of 40 ft span with 8 ft abutments, to two 20 ft arches with a central pier. Mackenzie felt this design was not of equal strength and thought himself most unfairly treated to be saddled with 'an engineering error' and yet held to blame for the failure by the 'Company, the Lawyer and the Engineer'.[17] Needless to say his account is at variance with that of Vignoles' biographers. Relations with Vignoles remained strained. Indeed, when discussing the maintenance of the permanent way on the Yarrow contract two years later, he wrote to Vignoles that he was unsure whether he would be able to fulfil this contract satisfactorily if Vignoles was to be the judge of what was satisfactory. Mackenzie still harboured a grudge over his earlier treatment and attacked Vignoles in no uncertain terms:

> an engineer of your changeable and flighty disposition ought never to come into contact with respectable contractors, but only with men of straw who have nothing to loose [sic] and those men who would fail in the execution of their contracts.[18]

When he was engaged for the Bishopton and Finlayston contracts of the Glasgow, Paisley and Greenock line, the pressure of work was becoming a problem and he possibly felt he had overreached himself. In a letter to John Errington, he wrote: ' I am wanted in Scotland and I am wanted here too, between one and another I have a hot shop. If purgatory is to be compared with it, I'll try and avoid it.'[19] Further evidence of the pressure of work came in a letter to William Betts early in 1839: 'My brother Edward will be married tomorrow [Wednesday], but he must go to work on Thursday.'[20] Edward Mackenzie married another Mary Dalziel, daughter of William Dalziel. Possibly she was the niece of his brother's first wife, who had died a month earlier. At the end of the year, William Mackenzie married his second wife Sarah Dewhurst.

By 1840, Mackenzie was stretching himself and his resources still further. In July there is the first mention of French contracts in an entry in his diary where he has noted a conversation with Locke about the Rouen railway. A month later Locke and Mackenzie travelled to France to hand in an estimate of £160,000. French engineers were keen to join with Mackenzie in a contracting venture, but he steered clear of such arrangements, not knowing their capabilities and experience.

M Nepveu visited Mackenzie and estimated for the Rolleboise tunnel with him. Later he and his family showed Mackenzie and his party the sights of Paris. Mackenzie was very impressed by the beautiful architecture and monuments of France and was obviously anxious to succeed in this great new venture and the opportunities it offered. Later Locke, Nepveu and Mackenzie visited the site of the Rolleboise tunnel and went on to Vernon and Rouen. Mackenzie was not used to the suspense of having to wait so long after a tender had been submitted to see if it was successful. Within a fortnight of returning to England, he politely wrote to Nepveu asking if 'our tender'[21] had been accepted.

During the next month, however, he was fully occupied with supervision of the Scottish works and tenders for the new works on the Shannon Navigation. He was eventually awarded the Killaloe, Mellick, Shannon, Banagher and Roorkey contracts which included several bridges, locks and weirs, together with dredging contracts. His association with the Shannon Commissioners proved to be entirely satisfactory to both parties. On completion of the contracts, the Commissioners voluntarily testified that he was the only contractor from whom they had been able to part without resorting to litigation of any kind. For his part, Mackenzie always maintained the Irish navvies he employed on the Shannon works were far superior to those he encountered elsewhere.[22]

The Mackenzie–Brassey partnership

It was towards the end of 1840 that William Mackenzie's connections with Thomas Brassey commenced. While inspecting the bridges and tunnels on the line near Paisley with Joseph Locke, John Errington and J Davidson, conversation must have turned to the subject of the French undertakings and, early in December, Mackenzie and Brassey discussed the French works, dissecting the prices of the Paris–Rouen tunnels. The following day they gave Locke further details, and suggested a price of £42 per linear yard. Locke offered £40. When Mackenzie offered to divide the difference at £41, Brassey confided to him later that he considered Mackenzie had been too rash in making a compromise offer so quickly. Mackenzie found himself in agreement as the deal was not completed.

After a further spell in Ireland, Mackenzie and Brassey met again in Chester and had further discussions. Two days later, on 6 January 1841, they settled with Locke, in the Grand Junction Railway Office in Liverpool, for the tunnels on the Paris–Rouen Railway, at the price Locke had originally offered. Mackenzie and Brassey were partners.

Soon money was being transferred to a bank in Paris and, in less than three weeks, they set sail for France. Within a month of their arrival they contracted for a short stretch of the Paris–Rouen Railway from St Germain to Poissy at a cost of £156,752 and finalised details of rails, timber, etc. Affairs in Scotland were never far from Mackenzie's thoughts, however. Six weeks later he was advising Locke about some of the costs of the proposed harbour improvements at Greenock, although a few days later when he saw Locke apparently seeking a second opinion, his diary underscores his intention 'to have no more to do with them!'.[23] Nevertheless four years later he undertook the Greenock Harbour works with Brassey and John Stephenson.

Back in England during the late spring and early summer of 1841, Mackenzie sorted out the organisation and financial arrangements of his remaining British works and drew up his will witnessed by W Dalziel and Samuel Holt (although unfortunately no copy of this early will has been found among his papers). When all the necessary arrangements had been made he returned to France with Brassey.

Further contracts on the Paris–Rouen followed, arranged by private treaty. Although at first they lost the contract for the Oissel bridge to a Frenchman, Locke asked them to give a revised estimate using concrete foundations, and Mackenzie offered a post on this work to J Smith of Portumna whom he had previously employed on the Shannon works.

In July 1841, Mackenzie and Brassey signed the deed of partnership of the engine manufactory at Rouen (Allcard, Buddicom and Co.) with capital of £50,000. Later that month Edward Mackenzie arrived to help supervise the works on the Paris–Rouen Railway. He and his family settled at Mantes, followed in 1842 by the Brassey family who settled initially at Vernon (William Mackenzie's base was in Paris).

The Mackenzie and Brassey partnership flourished, and in 1841 they tendered for many other contracts in France at the same time as they were maintaining their interests and successfully undertaking new contracts in Britain. Diaries exist for the whole of the period 1839–1853, showing the extent of their endeavours, their successes and failures. The many letterbooks, ledgers, letters, etc. in the collection need further research in order to paint the full picture of the partnership with Brassey and also with John Stephenson, as well as the contribution of Edward Mackenzie, and the working relationship with A H Neville (who features frequently in the diaries of the early 1840s and had the first patents for 'Warren' trusses), William Tite (who designed the stations and on occasions prepared other drawings for them), Errington, Davidson, Locke, etc.

Letterbooks and diaries show that Mackenzie was very frank in putting on paper his opinions regarding the engineers with whom he worked, no matter what their status or reputation. Even Locke did not escape criticism, for in 1841 Mackenzie noted the illiberality of the engineers on the Finlaystone contract and commented 'Locke has brought me in debt'.[24] On other occasions he commented on Locke's bouts of bad humour, recording on one occasion after Locke had flown into a rage that he 'ought to be ashamed of such conduct'.[25]

In January 1843, Mackenzie slipped on ice and suffered an accident which caused him much pain. Wrongly diagnosed as a bad sprain instead of broken bones, he was unable to put any weight on the foot for six weeks and the resulting weakness in his left foot and leg was to stay with him for the rest of his life. He often referred to his 'lame leg', but this in no way diminished his effectiveness or enthusiasm for the works in progress. A diary entry for 3 March 1843 records that his foot was still delicate and could not be used much, while that for the following day records that he 'hobbled to station at Poissy'. Two months later the whole line of Paris–Rouen Railway was opened throughout and what had previously been the Company's office in Rouen became the Rouen–Havre office as the line proceeded to Le Havre.

In the 1840s Mackenzie and Brassey together constructed three quarters of the French lines built, including the Orleans–Bordeaux, Amiens–Boulogne, Rouen–Dieppe as well as works in Spain and Britain.

Illness and death

In January 1848, William Mackenzie suffered an attack of gangrene which disabled him for three months. In December 1849 he was seriously ill once more, and the bone of his right toe was removed. His condition gradually deteriorated, the gangrene spread and eventually caused his death on 29 October 1851. It is an indication of his enthusiasm and fortitude that in the early stages of the condition he did not allow this disability to inhibit his usual pursuits. During the last two years of his life occasional loss of speech and loss of use of his right hand are recorded, indicating a stroke or seizure of some kind. His illness led to Thomas Brassey dissolving the partnership in 1850. Following his death, his brother Edward ensured the contracts they had undertaken were fulfilled, and in 1853 retired to a large country house near Henley. Edward Mackenzie continued to play an active role in railway financing for the rest of his life.

The legacy

In 1828 William Mackenzie was elected a member of the Institution of Civil Engineers and followed their meetings whenever he could. In 1843 he attended the conversazione of President James Walker and was introduced to Prince Albert and the Duke of Wellington. At the opening of the Tours and Poitiers section of the Orleans–Bordeaux Railway he was advised by Prince Louis Napoleon that it was intended to award him the Cross of the Legion of Honour. Unfortunately Mackenzie died before this honour could be bestowed upon him. Mackenzie's interest in Institution matters makes it particularly fitting that his papers are now with the Institution of Civil Engineers where they will be conserved and made available for research and study. An exhibition entitled 'Mackenzie: giant of the railways' has been held at the Institution of Civil Engineers to celebrate the bicentenary of his birth. A catalogue containing essays on the life and career of William Mackenzie, including an evaluation of his importance from the French point of view, has been published.[26]

There is a wealth of material to research in order to find out the full story. I hope to continue my own research, but I hope this indication of the scope of the collection will also encourage others to undertake further research into the Mackenzie collection. This is merely the tip of the iceberg.

Notes and references

1 'Obituary of William Mackenzie', *ICE Minutes of Proceedings*, XI (1852), p102
2 'Obituary of William Mackenzie', *Liverpool Mercury* (31 October 1851)
3 Helps, A, *Life and Labours of Mr Brassey, 1805–1870* (London: Bell and Daldy, 1872). This work has served Thomas Brassey well. Other nineteenth-century contractors were largely ignored; those who had biographies were mostly privately printed works, e.g. S M Peto, Thomas Jackson, James Falshaw; and the great names of the early nineteenth century, such as William John Joliffe, Edward Banks and Hugh McIntosh, have been totally ignored.
4 'Account of the bridge over the Severn, near the town of Tewkesbury, designed by Thomas Telford', *Transactions of the Institution of Civil Engineers*, 2 (1838), pp1–14
5 Drawing of Birmingham Canal. Section of proposed improvements at Smethwick Summit, Tipton Valley, and Bloomfield Deep (1830) and longitudinal section of feeder from Rotten Park Reservoir to the valley at Blue Gates (n.d.)
6 Drawing of Galton bridge at Smethwick (1830) and Spon Lane bridge (n.d.)
7 Drawing of ticket office, bridge and gauging locks (n.d.)
8 Mackenzie, W, *Letterbook* (1829–1840)
9 *ICE Minutes of Proceedings*, XI (1852), p103
10 Letter to Henry Booth, 7 July 1834, in Mackenzie, W, *Letterbook* (1829–1840)
11 Thomas, R H G, *The Liverpool and Manchester Railway* (London: Batsford, 1980), p118
12 Letter to Henry Booth, in Mackenzie, W, *Letterbook*

13 Letter to G McLeod, 23 August 1834, in Mackenzie, W, *Letterbook*
14 Letter to George Stephenson, 17 December 1833, in Mackenzie, W, *Letterbook*
15 Letter to Henry Booth, 26 June 1834, in Mackenzie, W, *Letterbook*
16 Letter to Sir Hardman Earle, 24 May 1836, in Mackenzie, W, *Letterbook*
17 Letter to H Tristram, 13 November 1837, in Mackenzie, W, *Letterbook*
18 Letter to C B Vignoles, 4 September 1839, in Mackenzie, W, *Letterbook*
19 Letter to John Errington, 24 September 1838, in Mackenzie, W, *Letterbook*
20 Letter to William Betts, 29 January 1839, in Mackenzie, W, *Letterbook*
21 Letter to M Nepveu, 11 September 1840, in Mackenzie, W, *Letterbook*
22 Mackenzie, W, *Diary* (22 October 1847)
23 Mackenzie, W, *Diary* (3 April 1841)
24 Mackenzie, W, *Diary* (31 August 1841)
25 Mackenzie, W, *Diary* (12 March 1843)
26 Chrimis, M M, Murphy, M K and Ribeill, G. Mackenzie — giant of the railways: William Mackenzie (1794–1851) and the construction of the early European railway network (London: Institution of Civil Engineers, 1994)

Additional reading

Baughan, P E, *The Chester and Holyhead Railway* (Newton Abbot: David & Charles, 1972), 1

Brooke, D, *The Railway Navvie* (Newton Abbot: David & Charles, 1981)

Burton, A, *The Canal Builders* (London: Eyre Methuen, 1972)

Burton, A, *The Railway Builders* (London: John Murray, 1992)

Coleman, T, *The Railway Navvies: a History of the Men Who Made the Railways* (London: Hutchinson, 1965)

Devey, J, *The Life of Joseph Locke, Civil Engineer* (London: Bentley, 1862)

Henderson, W O, *Britain and Industrial Europe 1750–1870: Studies in British Influence on the Industrial Revolution in Western Europe* (Leicester: Leicester University Press, 1972)

Jeaffreson, J C, *The Life of Robert Stephenson, with Descriptive Chapters on Some of his Most Important Professional Works by W Pole* (London: Longman, 1864)

Joby, R S, *The Railway Builders: Lives and Works of the Victorian Railway Contractors* (Newton Abbot: David & Charles, 1983)

Marshall, J, *A Biographical Dictionary of Railway Engineers* (Newton Abbot: David & Charles, 1978)

Marshall, J, *The Lancashire and Yorkshire Railway* (Newton Abbot: David & Charles, 1969), 1

Osborne, E C and Osborne, W, *Osborne's London and Birmingham Railway Guide* (Birmingham: E C & W Osborne, 1838)

Parry, E, *Parry's Railways Companion from Chester to Holyhead* (London: A Hall, 1848)

Reed, B, *Crewe to Carlisle* (London: Ian Allan, 1969)

Roscoe, T, *Home and Country Scenes on Each Side of the Line of the London and Birmingham and Grand Junction Railway* (London: C Tilt, 1839)

Roscoe, T, *The London and Birmingham Railway: with the Home and Country Scenes on Each Side of the Line* (London: C Tilt, 1839)

Vignoles, K H, *Charles Blacker Vignoles: Romantic Engineer* (Cambridge: Cambridge University Press, 1982)

Vignoles, O J, *Life of Charles Blacker Vignoles . . . a Reminiscence of Early Railway History* (London: Longmans, 1889)

Webster, N W, *Britain's First Trunk Line* (Bath: Adams and Dart, 1972)

Webster, N W, *Joseph Locke: Railway Revolutionary* (London: Allen and Unwin, 1970)

Overshadowed—the case of David Elder

James L Wood

The leading light in the rise of marine engineering and shipbuilding as major nineteenth-century industries on the Clyde was, without doubt, Robert Napier.[1] He started his business career in 1815 by taking over a small blacksmith's business in Glasgow. He took on two apprentices to help him. At the time of his death in 1876 his firm employed 3000 people. Of course no business of that size could be a one-man band and leading lights need fuel. He was helped at various times by several relatives, notably his brother James and his two sons James Robert, and John.

Many of the next generation of engineers also worked for him in the formative years of their careers and then went on to achieve fame and fortune elsewhere. Among them were Charles Randolph, John Elder, James and George Thomson, William Pearce, Walter Brock, Alexander Kirk, David Kirkaldy, Hugh Dunsmuir and William Jackson. Some of them later set up in competition with Napier, and with all the advantages of youth on their side they achieved considerable success. These men gained the knowledge and experience necessary for their subsequent careers during the relatively short periods they spent with Robert Napier.

However, there was another, David Elder, who worked with him for about forty years and created the solid foundation on which the success of Napier's business was built. Elder is almost unknown nowadays and his work largely unrecognised. Yet the writer of an obituary notice for his son John, of compound-engine fame, who died in 1869 only three years after his father, wrote:

> His father, the late David Elder, was long and well known as the manager of the great engineering establishment of Mr Robert Napier, Glasgow. The old man possessed an abundance of professional skill of so rare a kind as almost to be entitled to the appellation of genius; and under him his son gained the insight which ultimately fructified so largely as to gain for him the high position which he occupied at the time of his death. It would be difficult to say where marine engineering would have been if the two Elders had not lived; we scarcely think that it would be possible to name any two persons who, together, have done more to raise the reputation of the Clyde in the department of marine engineering and to advance that art to the rank of one of the exact sciences.[2]

In 1879, the writer of an obituary for James R Napier remarked that the Robert Napier works

> has a sort of classical history attaching to it as a great engineering school, in which the head master was not really Robert Napier, but David Elder, father of the late John Elder, and one of the most accomplished mechanics that ever held a place of trust in any workshop on the Clyde.[3]

That these two writers should have such lengthy asides on the merits of David Elder certainly suggests that he was appreciated in his own time.

It is not my purpose to play down the importance of Robert Napier in any way. His achievements speak for themselves. The aim is rather to draw attention to Elder's contribution to Napier's success and to comment on the relationship between them.

The beginnings of marine engineering on the Clyde

The importance of nineteenth-century shipbuilding and marine engineering to the Scottish economy is beyond doubt. At its peak it provided employment for perhaps a quarter of the total workforce, both directly and in dependent industries. It was the sunrise industry of the time, its growth the result of cheap labour and raw materials, and new technology.

Although William Symington had built workable steam-boats on the Forth & Clyde Canal in the early years of the nineteenth century, his experiments led to little but disappointment. It was Henry Bell's *Comet* of 1812 which showed that the steamer had a commercial future. The *Comet*, like Newcomen's engine, was a novel combination of well-established technologies rather than something completely new. At that time Glasgow was a rapidly growing manufacturing centre, based largely on the cotton industry, and the construction of engines and boilers for the growing number of steam-powered factories was a regular business. Wooden shipbuilding was likewise well established on the Clyde. All the essential ingredients for a steam-boat were there. It did not require any new inventions; it simply needed an entrepreneur, someone who realised that uniting these elements might be a paying proposition and had the courage to place an order.

The *Comet* remained in service on various routes on the Clyde until it was wrecked at Crinan in 1820. By 1832 there were fifty-nine steamers in service on the Clyde alone. Many others had been built on the Clyde for service on coastal and short sea routes elsewhere. Among the engineers involved in the new marine engineering industry were Caird & Co., James Cook, Claud Girdwood, Duncan MacArthur, and David and Robert Napier.

David and Robert Napier

Of those mentioned above, the two Napiers are by far the most important and best known. Although they were cousins, both born in Dumbarton, and their businesses were to have historical links through the use of the same premises at different times, they never worked in partnership. Of the fifty-nine vessels noted in 1832, sixteen had been engined by David Napier and eleven by Robert.

David Napier began marine engine building in 1816, five years ahead of his cousin. He was quickly recognised as a clever engineer and, in the early years of the industry on the Clyde, he was more influential than Robert.

Robert Napier was perhaps less inventive as an engineer than David, but he was a much better businessman and entrepreneur. He was born in 1791. His father, James Napier, was a blacksmith and worked with John Napier, father of David. Robert began his working life formally apprenticed to his father. Then in 1811 he went to Edinburgh for a spell, returning to Dumbarton to work once more with his father. After some time in Glasgow with William Lang, who made equipment for the textile industry, he acquired a small blacksmith's business in the city, in Greyfriars Wynd, in 1815.

In 1821, Robert Napier moved into a works at Camlachie in the east of Glasgow, which had been occupied by David until he went to a new site at Lancefield. There he began to build steam engines. Of this new venture David Napier later wrote, 'I let [the Camlachie works] to my cousin, Robert Napier, who, having obtained the assistance of a clever mechanic of the name of Elder, commenced to make engines at my old premises at Camlachie with very great success.'[4] The 'clever mechanic' was David Elder.

The first engine was for a flax-spinning mill in Dundee. Then in 1823 came the first for a ship, a single cylinder side-lever engine for the wooden vessel *Leven* built by William Denny, Dumbarton.

In 1828 Robert Napier took over an existing works in Washington Street, nearer the River Clyde. As the Vulcan Foundry, this was to become very well known throughout the world of nineteenth-century marine engineering. In addition, late in 1835, he rented the Lancefield Works from his cousin David who had decided to move to London.

Robert Napier built up a reputation for first-class work, supplying engines for a wide variety of steamers including many for the companies set up to operate services between Scotland, England and Ireland. There was a major breakthrough in 1836 when Napier obtained the order for his first ocean-going ship, the *Berenice,* a paddle steamer with side-lever engines of 250 nominal horse power for the Honourable East India Company. As with many of these early orders, Napier was the prime contractor. The building of the wooden hull was subcontracted, in this case to John Wood of Port Glasgow.

The influential customer was well pleased with the ship and the success of the *Berenice* was to lead to greater things. When Samuel Cunard was awarded a contract by the Admiralty for a transatlantic mail service by steamship he was introduced to Robert Napier by James Melvill, Secretary to the Honourable East India Company. As a result, four ships were ordered from Napier in 1839. But Napier did more than agree to provide Samuel Cunard with ships; he introduced him to the business community in Glasgow. This resulted in the setting up of the British and North American Royal Mail Steam Packet Company with a capital of £270,000, subscribed by thirty-three individuals including Cunard and Napier himself. That he was able to do this with little apparent difficulty is an indication of his commercial status, and of the profits already being made in shipping and other industries in the area.

The successful completion of the *Berenice* contract also helped Napier in his efforts to obtain contracts from the Admiralty. In 1838 he was given the order for the machinery for two dockyard-built wooden paddle sloops, *Vesuvius* and *Stromboli*. Thereafter he engined many other naval vessels for both the British and various foreign governments.

In 1841 Napier acquired ground at Govan, on the south side of the Clyde (Vulcan and Lancefield works were both on the north side), for an iron shipbuilding yard. The first ship was completed two years later. The first naval contract for an iron hull was for the *Simoom*, of 1849, which was engined by Matthew Boulton and James Watt. A notable contract was for the hull of the *Black Prince*, of 1861, sister ship to the *Warrior*. Both vessels were engined by John Penn. For the *Hector* of 1862, a shortened version of *Black Prince* and *Warrior*, Napier was contracted to build both the hull and the machinery. This was probably the first time that a such a contract for a warship, complete with its machinery, had been given to a private builder.

By the early 1860s the firm had reached its peak and thereafter it was, to some extent, living on its reputation. When Robert Napier died in 1876, the business had been in financial difficulty for some years. No members of the family wanted to take it over and in 1877 it was sold to a partnership headed by an ex-Napier apprentice, A C Kirk. The new partnership proposed to tender for a less prestigious class of work.

David Elder

The principal source of information about David Elder is the *Memoir of the Late David Elder*. This was read to the Institution of Engineers in Scotland a week after Elder's death on 7 February 1866, by James R Napier, Robert Napier's elder son, and subsequently published in *The Engineer*.[5]

Like so many of the first-generation Scottish engineers, Elder's background was that of a country millwright. He was born in January 1785 at Little Seggie, near Kinross. At the age of fifteen he started to learn his father's business. Because of the religious strife to which the church in Scotland was prone, he was not able to attend the parish school. His formal education was therefore sparse and he was largely self-taught. He must have been determined to learn because he travelled eighteen miles to borrow a book on algebra and then had to conceal it from his father who had no great opinion of book learning.

He found country millwrighting somewhat restrictive, and in 1804 he was in Edinburgh on building work in the New Town. He continued his education by borrowing books at a penny a night from a bookstall in the High Street.

By 1814 he had married and was working for J Clark & Co. of Paisley. Soon afterwards he superintended the building of a new spinning mill for them at Mile End, Glasgow. Subsequently he was employed by James Dunlop, in the erection of Broomward mill, also in Glasgow.

About 1820, James Napier says mysteriously, 'he [Elder] appears to have made a business connection which was unsatisfactory to himself', but there is no hint as to what this might have been. In 1821 he joined Robert Napier as manager of his works at Camlachie and was involved in the design and construction of the first marine engine, for the *Leven* of 1823.

Elder's technical contributions to marine engineering can be dealt with in two groups, although James Napier does not so divide them. The first can be classed as detail design improvements. It is difficult to be certain of the extent to which Elder pioneered such changes in advance of other engineers, without knowing more about the normal practice of his contemporaries. He may simply have been flowing with the tide to some extent. Some of them appear self-evident but then hindsight is a wonderful thing. The following are among those specifically mentioned by his biographer.

- The 'long D' slide valves used on many engines were 'lengthened upwards and downwards beyond the face, so as to get the packing immediately opposite the port, thereby reducing the pressure both upon the valve face and packing.' Less power was required to drive the valve, and the cost of keeping the packing in order was reduced. (Plate 6)
- Cushioning of the piston at the end of the exhaust stroke was arranged by 'the cover which he invariably put on the eduction side of the valve'. In more modern terminology he used 'exhaust lap' on the valves so that the port was closed to the exhaust steam before the piston reached the end of its stroke.
- Elder used larger steam ports than was normal. He realised that the port size should be governed by the volume of the exhaust steam which, because of its lower pressure, had a greater volume than the live steam.
- Separate expansion valves were introduced, allowing ready alteration of cut-off point for the

admission of steam to the cylinder. These were probably first used on the *Berenice*.

- Air pump efficiency was increased by lowering the working barrel almost to the bottom of the suction well. 'However self-evident such an arrangement may appear now, or when pointed out, a different practice was followed in the marine engines of the period preceding the commencement of Mr Elder's career.'
- The top of the hot well, into which the air pump discharged, was raised and enclosed. There was also an overflow pipe leading overboard. This was the result of experience gained the hard way as Elder was scalded when the hot well overflowed on the *Eclipse*, built in 1826 for the Glasgow to Belfast service.

The second group of technical innovations consists of essentially manufacturing improvements. When Elder set about building the *Leven* engine the tools available were limited to a few 10–14-inch lathes with wooden shears (beds), 'a rude horizontal boring mill' and a vertical boring machine. In due course he developed several special purpose machine tools to improve productivity and to render him less dependent on 'those who rebelled against his system, and would have compelled him to adopt theirs.'

Elder held strong views on the need for rigidity in the frames, with the strength of the machinery being independent of the hull of the ship. As James Napier said, 'Competing vessels on the Atlantic line (i.e. those competing with the Cunard vessels engined by Napier) had their engine frames broken probably from the weakness and twisting of the vessel.'

As might have been expected, there was difficulty in finding workmen prepared to work to the required standard. He did not consider the work of the old-style millwrights to be good enough and much preferred to recruit good cartwrights or house joiners 'believing they would carry their ideas of close-fitting joints in wooden structures along with them when they would be called upon to construct iron ones.' Indeed he had such a high opinion of the joinery trade that when A C Kirk was interviewed as a prospective apprentice he was told to work as a joiner for two years and then come back and begin engineering.[6] Kirk did as he was advised and later said that he never regretted the time thus spent.

In 1833 Elder devised a paring machine, which was a form of milling machine, to finish the straps of the connecting and side rods. (Plate 7) This was many years before milling machines came into general use. In part the incentive seems to have been industrial trouble as it was used to do 'the work of those legal hands, as they called themselves, who had combined to stop the works by their union.' He designed a copying attachment for a lathe for forming the curved fish-belly shape of rods and crossheads. (Plate 8) This greatly reduced the time taken to machine these components.

All joints in the engine frames were metal to metal, with the bolts draw-filed and fitted to the holes, and seats for all bolts and nuts made fair. As James Napier wrote:

> His cast iron Gothic frames, so well known for their elegance and simplicity could be well secured to the sole plate, and to each other, by flanges and bolts of any dimensions; and the two engines could be similarly secured to each other, so that, let the ship roll and pitch, and perhaps twist, as she might, the engine was not to twist, it was not to be affected in the least degree possible by the probable twisting of the vessel.[7]

Also in the interests of rigidity 'he continued the sole plate under the cylinder, and was the first (in the author's belief) to do so.'

In the case of the machinery for HMS *Thunderbolt*, of 1842, probably the first built by Napier to have malleable iron bar frames, instead of cast iron, the holes for the columns in the sole plate and entablature were bored using the same template and the column ends turned and draw-filed to fit the holes. Although not specifically mentioned, it is likely that the same procedure was used for other engines with malleable iron bar frames.

The all-important main centre of the side-lever engines, on which the levers pivoted, was fixed into a tube cast in the condenser. This avoided the need for an air-tight gland where the centre passed through the condenser and eliminated the possibility of air leaks into the condenser at this point. (Plate 9) The tube was taper bored by a self-acting boring bar devised by Elder, and the centre 'thoroughly driven home by the force of large rams suspended from the ceiling of the fitting shop'.

The first group of improvements discussed above are all relatively minor when regarded individually, but taken together they resulted in a significantly better engine. They were the product of a mind always searching for improved ways of doing things. But Elder's most important contribution to the reputation and prosperity of the firm was his concern for rigid design and construction and first-class workmanship in everything which was produced. At the same time he was not slow to increase productivity by the use of such devices as the paring machine and the lathe copying attachment.

When the first two naval vessels with Napier engines, *Vesuvius* and *Stromboli*, had been in service for a short time, Napier arranged for a question to be asked in Parliament, seeking a statement of the names of engine builders who had supplied machinery to the Admiralty, together with information on initial costs, cost of repairs and time out of service for repairs.[8] For the *Vesuvius* and *Stromboli*, the repair costs per day in commission, 10d (4.2p) and 1/5¼d (7.2p) respectively, compared very favourably with the products of Seaward at almost £1 and Maudslay at over 10/– (50p). Obviously it would be unwise to accept these figures wholeheartedly at face value, without further information, but they do suggest that Napier's engines had something the others may have lacked. This was the Elder touch, the overriding concern for rigid design of the engine frames and a high standard of workmanship.

This episode illustrates another reason for Napier's success in business. He had the personal qualities with which he could establish and maintain the sort of connections which enabled him to plant questions in Parliament.

The Napier family and David Elder

As the main source of information about David Elder is James Napier's Memoir it is necessary to consider what he says in the light of his relationship with Elder and his position in the family firm.

The Memoir is very much a eulogy. James Napier was trained by Elder and clearly held him in great esteem. In writing the Memoir he was very concerned that his contribution to the prosperity of the family firm should not go unrecognised. He concludes by saying

> Mr Elder's connection with Mr Robert Napier was a happy one for himself, and a fortunate one for Mr Napier and his family. When, some years ago, he ceased to be actively employed by the new firm of R Napier and Sons it was a very great grief to himself, and an irreparable loss to the author.

James Napier was born in 1821.[9] He went to the High School of Glasgow and then to the University of Glasgow where he studied mathematics, natural philosophy and astronomy. Thereafter he became 'a diligent and apt pupil' of Elder. In due course he was put in charge of the shipbuilding yard at Govan. It would seem that he had neither the business ability nor indeed the interest in business of his father but 'was possessed of high scientific attainments'. In 1850 he joined the Philosophical Society of Glasgow and contributed many papers to its *Proceedings*. He undertook important work on the strains in iron vessels and collaborated with Professor W J Macquorn Rankine and others in the massive treatise *Shipbuilding Theoretical and Practical*, published in 1866.[10]

James Napier and his younger brother John were taken into partnership in 1853 and the firm became Robert Napier and Sons. Robert Napier had intended to retire from active management of the business at this stage. However, the new partnership did not work out and James left in 1857. Robert returned to active management and he and John remained the only partners until his death in 1876, after which the business was sold.

Although Elder never became a partner he was clearly highly regarded by Robert Napier. Perhaps he never wanted a partnership, with its unlimited liability for the debts of the concern. As an indispensable employee he was generously rewarded. Details survive of the terms under which he was employed in the 1830s. He entered into a new seven-year agreement[11] with Robert Napier in 1835 whereby he was paid £250 per annum plus 7/6d (37.5p) for each Nominal Horse Power his employer contracted for. This could amount to a substantial sum. For example the contracts for the first four Cunard vessels of 420 NHP each, or 1680 NHP in total, were worth £630 to David Elder, over and above his salary. This agreement was renewed for a further five years and we find Robert Napier writing to a friend, Mr Moncreiff, in November 1842:

> You will perceive Mr Elder and I have arranged, in the spirit of true friendship, for a lease of each other's services for five years, if we are spared together for so long. If all is right with both of us, it should nearly, I think, terminate the laborious and active part of our lives.

But this was not to be. Robert Napier continued to take an active part in the business into the 1860s, although he was over seventy years old by then. This was despite his new country mansion at West Shandon and his interest in the growing art collection there. James having gone his own way in 1857, his brother John increasingly took charge of the business.

There are hints that in earlier years John Napier did not see eye to eye with Elder in technical matters.[12] John had 'modern ideas of light machinery but these were not favourably considered by his father's manager Mr Elder. At that time John Napier rarely got an opportunity of showing what could be done . . .'.

It seems likely that as John Napier became, in effect, the managing partner, the boot would have been on the other foot. Elder, like Robert Napier, was getting on in years. By then even less likely to welcome new ideas, he was eased out of the business some time after James Napier's departure. There is no indication that he had any interests beyond work and no doubt he felt it keenly. Robert Napier and Elder had built up the business together over a period of forty years. They were set in their ways and, while sad, it is not surprising that plans for the succession did not work out.

Whatever the problems in later years, there can be little doubt that the role of Elder was crucial to Robert Napier's success. The orders were won by the energy, personality, personal contacts and commercial skills of Robert Napier himself, but it was David Elder, the 'clever mechanic', who was responsible for the high standards of construction and design, which made the reputation of the firm.

Notes and references

1 The introductory material on Clyde marine engineering and on Robert Napier is condensed from, Wood, J L, 'Scottish marine engineering: the first fifty years', *Transactions of the Newcomen Society*, 64 (1992–1993), pp77–99

2 'The late Mr John Elder', *Engineering*, 8 (1869), p213

3 'The late Mr James R Napier, FRS', *Engineering*, 28 (1879), p497

4 Napier, D D (ed), *David Napier, Engineer, 1790–1869, an Autobiographical Sketch with Notes* (Glasgow: James Maclehose, 1912), p2

5 Napier, J R, 'Memoir of the late Mr David Elder, engineer', *The Engineer*, 21 (1866), pp256–57

6 'Alexander C Kirk', *The Engineer*, 74 (1892), p312

7 Napier, J R, p256

8 Wood, J L, p90

9 Anon., 'The late Mr James R Napier'

10 Macquorn Rankine, W J (ed), *Shipbuilding Theoretical and Practical* (Glasgow: W Mackenzie, 1866)

11 Napier, J, *Life of Robert Napier of West Shandon* (Edinburgh: William Blackwood, 1904), pp85–86

12 Napier, J, pp44–45

Strategic technology and the history of engineering

M C Duffy

Analyses of the perception of engineers necessitate setting the changing nature of engineering in a historical perspective, and relating it to an evolving understanding of the characteristic features of sound historical analysis.[1] History, as a method of analysis, and engineering have changed in nature. In particular, those strategic technologies which give engineering its exemplars, have changed radically during distinct periods of change in history, and each phase of transformation has led to a time of economic growth during which new archetypes of engineer, system and methods have emerged.[2]

Paralleling this endless transformation of the nature of engineering is a change in the methods of analysing the past. Generally, most historians have been ignorant about the nature of engineering and its method,[3] and non-historian writers about history of technology have, in the main, neglected questions of method and drawn no lessons from the history of history.[4] Both groups have neglected philosophy, and their works have lacked definitions of engineering method which are vital for identifying and classifying the several kinds of engineer. Granted the severe limitations on space, all I can do is refer the reader to sources and present the most compressed account of those general features of the history of history which have affected the way writers about engineering have seen history, engineering, history of engineering and history of engineers.

It must always be remembered that the popular interpretation of a philosophy (for example that of Hegel), or of a scientific theory (such as Darwinian evolution), is usually crudely distorted and simplified. The popular conception of engineers and engineering is in part the result of a vulgarisation of ideas originating in theology, philosophy, economics and theories of history.

The influence of history of religion

In European culture, before the Enlightenment and before the spread of secular humanism established rational, scientific method as the norm in scholarly matters during the seventeenth century, exemplary historical works were largely religious. The concept of historical study, with its goals, subjects and objects, and methods and standards, developed within a religious framework which was still a powerful influence while an expanding economy, reliant on powered mechanised industry, was being introduced.

The first great histories of the Christian epoch met the need for a perspective, codified and regulated, of a given truth — presumed to be revealed by God — which needed to be preserved and promulgated once a church organisation had appeared which sought to preserve itself as its origins receded into the past.[5] The *Ecclesiastical History* of Eusebius, born in the mid-third century, introduced the model for style and methods which was followed by Socrates the Lawyer, Sozomen the Lawyer, and Bishop Theodoret of Cyprus in the fourth to sixth centuries. It became the model for church history, with its attempt to record with accuracy a given truth. It is interesting in its use of synchronous tables and eyewitness accounts.

Post-Reformation times witnessed the compilation of influential archetypal 'histories' which presented different interpretations of what was supposed to be a given truth. The *Magdeburg Centuries*, compiled after 1559 by Matthias Flacius Illyricus (b1520), and the *Annales Ecclesiastici*, written as a response after 1588 by Caesar, Cardinal Baronius (b1538), were influential in setting standards for determining what constituted a sound, scholarly, wide-ranging historical study.

The *Magdeburg Centuries* of Illyricus was structured so that it dealt with its theme of general church history by centuries, each subdivided into topics. This helped to establish a pattern followed by later writers of comprehensive works, not least in history of technology, but it is a pattern which influences interpretation, depending on how the separate themes are defined and inter-related.[6]

The *Annales Ecclesiastici* of Cardinal Baronius was presented as a non-partisan account of the Christian past, with the accent on truth and accuracy, although it was as partisan as any of the great treatises of its time. Its structure differed from that of the *Magdeburg Centuries*, as it concentrated more on enduring institutions, like the papacy, and their effects, thus exemplifying another major pattern found in historical works that cover a wide field and a long time period.[7]

Gottfried Arnold (1666–1714) wrote from a new perspective, presenting his work under the heading 'Non-partisan church history and the history of heretics from the beginning of the New Testament to the year of Our Lord 1688'. By this time, rational method was becoming exemplary, and secular culture was growing. However, the methods of history established during the Christian epoch remained influential, as did much of the metaphysics associated with orthodox Christian dogmatics. They continued to influence historical studies, philosophy and the sciences into the nineteenth century, sometimes indirectly. Radically transformed and developed by atheists, humanists and theologically revolutionary Christian philosophers, these notions continued to shape history and the sciences for much of the nineteenth century.

During this early period, long before the Enlightenment, much of strategic engineering was the consequence of 'secularising celestial or cosmic goals', i.e. it resulted from seeking to replicate in mechanism the physical and even metaphysical (or occult) properties of the cosmos. The quest for perpetual motion machines comes into this category, because these devices sought to reproduce the 'perfect, perpetual motions' of the celestial spheres.[8] The substances from which components of mechanisms were made had occult properties, being related to individual planets or signs of the zodiac. The long progress to a rational, scientific vision of the universe is revealed in the steady ridding of engineering, cosmology, medicine and chemistry of occult, magical or metaphysical attributes.[9]

The contribution of engineering to the rational perception of the universe, and its part in lifting the curses of superstition and uncritical supernaturalism, have been overlooked by most writers, who give all the credit to that curious invention of the nineteenth century known as 'pure science'. The radical philosopher of religion, D Cupitt, is one of the few to acknowledge that man's experience with machinery changed his relationship with natural phenomena, and led him to regard the universe as a machine, regulated by natural law, free from occult intervention.[10] The almost total absence of any serious study of the contributions made by engineering to theology and philosophy is further evidence of the gross misrepresentation of the role of engineering in western culture which has arisen, in part, from the misconception of the nature of engineering itself.

In the Enlightenment, engineering metaphors became common, and mechanical models and analogues were a feature of the mechanical world view.[11] Occult metaphysical attributes were eliminated from models, and metaphysics became more rational. The 'secularising of goals' continued as an enduring theme in engineering, with fruitful results of global significance.

More than one engineer, between the seventeenth and twentieth century, sought to replicate in mechanism, or in the organisation of an industry, the order and harmony discovered in the natural universe using rational method. This replicating an underlying harmony by eliminating 'bad fit' of components led to the rational machine theory of J Leupold, Lazare Carnot, F Reuleaux, and G V Lomonossoff, but, perhaps more importantly, it led to rational theories of organising mechanised industrial activity as practised by F W Taylor, H L Gantt, F B Gilbreth and H Ford.[12]

These theories played a major part in fostering the belief that scientific investigation of nature revealed goals worthy of pursuit, and discovered methods worthy of application, which strengthened faith in progress through science, engineering and rational organisation.

Engineering itself encouraged the idea of progress by presenting mankind with the example of improved designs of machines and improved levels of performance within the lifetimes of individual engineers. The treatises of Branca, Zonca and Ramelli contained descriptions of devices including those which were centuries old.[13] There was considerable progress before 1500, but it was steady. Radically new inventions, such as the weight-driven clock and the cannon, were rare, but by 1700 innovation was common enough to establish change, innovation, progress, discovery and widespread transformation as distinct concepts applicable to industrial activity.[14] Clearly, the religious upheavals of the Reformation helped gain acceptance for the idea that radical political, philosophical, and social change was possible, perhaps inevitable, but the role of technology in encouraging this mental tradition should not be underrated.

Technology was no mere derived activity, created by socio-political change. It was the source of many of these changes.

Historicism, romanticism and evolutionism

The increasing influence of a secularised eschatology; the growth of popular evolutionism (always to be distinguished from evolutionary theories); and natural theology made it easier to accept that the society, science, philosophy and human activity of the future were not predefined by some revelation in the past, as Eusebius supposed, but were created by acts of will. Man and his creations changed, and evolving science, technology and industry were agents for introducing future states which could be planned and chosen within the constraints of natural law. Progress became a recognised phenomenon, and the jealous theistic God of the Judaeo-Christian theologies gave way to the self-effacing rational lawgiver of eighteenth-century deism, or the immanent 'god' of the radical philosophers who followed Hegel.[15] Hegel's philosophy has been grossly distorted and misrepresented by popular writers and politicians, although the criticisms of his positions — as put for example by Camus — remain valid.[16]

However unfair it may be to link Hegel's concept of history and virtue to the popular-historicist movements of totalitarian Russia and Germany, it seems clear that it was largely from his work that the notion of the 'world-historical' figure entered popular consciousness in the early nineteenth century. Popular historicism accepted that there are drives in history, so that history unfolds as if impelled towards some inevitable destiny by some mysterious immanent power.[17] This immanent 'god' was supposed to work towards a future in which some goal (identified by the believer's party programme or faith) was realised. This might take the form of a liberal utopia, a world dominated by the Aryan race, or the victory of the proletariat. Individuals, including engineers, either were classified as willing agents who put themselves on the side of progress (the working out of the purpose of history) or were condemned as wilful reactionaries who deliberately hindered the chosen group, race, nation or party from gaining its destiny. Nations dominated by overtly historicist policies, chiefly Stalin's Russia, and Hitler's Germany, regarded engineers as agents of historicism, with success or failure in design interpreted not only as measures of loyalty, but as evidence of the degree to which engineers had given themselves over to fulfilling the destiny of party, race or state.

In Great Britain, where historicism never became totalitarian, the idea of world-historical figures was popularised through the Germanophile writings of Thomas Carlyle, with his 'great man' approach to history.[18] The influence of romanticism and its emphasis on the great individual, romantic history, significant incident, nationalism, and the myth of the gifted agent of destiny, reinforced historicism. Popular beliefs were that 'history is written by great men' and (a more dangerous idea) that great men become great by acting out the destiny preordained by whichever immanent force shaped the universe.

This was a dominant idea in the early nineteenth century, and, although it was strongly resisted, it shaped many of the early histories of engineering, which were written by men who were not sufficiently aware of philosophy, or historical analysis, to guard against the influence of an eclectic mixture of Hegelian philosophy, historicism, 'great-man history' and romanticism. The result was usually some form of engineering 'Whiggery', which interpreted the past as the road to an inevitable present.[19] The historicists stressed the myth of progress as a drama of world-historic figures. Others, less Hegelian, still portrayed history as the creation of strong-willed, free-choosing great men, sometimes to the exclusion of other interpretations. Samuel Smiles comes into this camp.[20] Because of this, one might have expected the engineer to emerge as the most respected figure of nineteenth-century Britain. Some writers, such as Smiles, did so regard him:

> What is England without its tools, its machinery, its steam-engine, its steam-ships, and its locomotive? Are not the men who have made the motive power of the country, and immensely increased its productive strength, the men above all who have . . . [made] . . . the country what it is?[21]

But as C Barnett[22] and M J Wiener[23] noted, there were powerful cultural forces at work which encouraged ill-informed prejudices against engineering and industry. T B Macaulay, R Cobden, Smiles and others saw science and engineering as major agents of cultural progress, but they were opposed by those whose deep ignorance concerning technology and industry rendered them incapable of recognising in engineering an exacting discipline through which new creative powers were finding expression. J Ruskin, M Arnold, J H Newman and their kind, laying much of the blame for the sins of commercial enterprise on mechanised industry, shaped the ideals of British education after the mid-nineteenth century. These ideals enjoyed widespread acceptance until the 1960s, and they were anti-science, anti-engineering, anti-trade, anti-industry and anti-progress. They were part of a reaction against new ideas, such as the 'new theology' which developed after 1700, and which flourished in Germany during the nineteenth century whilst being resisted in Britain. Throughout the nineteenth century, Britain became dangerously backward in several vital intellectual departments.

The profound ignorance concerning the nature of engineering resulted in a tendency to regard engineers as standing outside the scientific tradition, on the grounds that what they did had nothing to do with deepening understanding of the nature of things: an attitude which would have been incomprehensible to seventeenth- and eighteenth-century engineers such as C Polhem and J Leupold. Science in the sense of pure science gained some acceptance in British nineteenth-century culture, especially once it presented itself as an interpretation of truth via beautiful theoretical structures, although this acceptance was often grudgingly given. The myth of pure science set up a ranking order of 'scientific activity' which endures. Philosophy ranked highest because it sought deeper understanding of the nature of things: philosophers sought truth. Pure science ranked second, with preference given to those sciences which raised philosophical issues — such as cosmology. The worst feature of the 'pure science myth' was the unsupported assumption, born out of prejudice and ignorance of the history of engineering, that engineering is applied science rather than a science in its own right through which understanding of the nature of things is increased.

According to this system of values, engineering therefore ranked much lower than pure science, and was further condemned by its association with mechanised industry, which was held up as the embodiment of Mammon worship and philistinism by the Arnolds and Newmans and their still more ignorant and dishonest acolytes.[24] By becoming associated with the pursuit of truth (a 'non-worldly' concept), science was able to gain in prestige once the world of education, and the churches, had come to terms with geology, evolution, cosmology — which they did rapidly whilst remaining conservative. Once the conservatives recognised that science was not intrinsically hostile to religion or morality, science enjoyed a higher status than did engineering which remained linked to the 'merely mundane'. It was not an instrument through which knowledge could be obtained. It was condemned as a means of getting 'know-how', fit only for the uncultivated mechanic, who was also regarded as a threat to an older culture which it was the duty of the cultivated gentleman to defend. The situation is savagely satirised by Mark Twain in *Connecticut Yankee* which portrays the impact of the ignorant mechanic, Hank Morgan, on an ancient feudal society.[25]

In Britain, the defence of this older culture — seen through a distorted perspective by the escapist conservatives — was an effective one, resulting in a neglect of engineering by the academic historian and philosopher which continues to the present. The lack of adequate, analytical histories of engineering, the absence of a philosophy of technology based on a definition of engineering method, and the lack of understanding of the nature of engineering by those economists and historians who have tried to comprehend it, can be traced to this mid-nineteenth-century failure of mind. The great contributions made by Professor D S L Cardwell to remedy this deficiency, by presenting engineering and industrial activity as scientific disciplines in their own right, mark — one hopes — the founding of a British school of engineering history which will at last correct the distortions of over a century of ignorance, largely because its work is done by those who understand science and engineering, who have professional experience of it, and who have also been educated in the methods of academic historical analysis.[26]

There are also signs that the philosopher–engineer, who was usual before the nineteenth century, is becoming recognised once more, as the changing nature of late twentieth-century technology makes his activities increasingly necessary and obvious, in such exemplary fields as advanced bioelectronics, neuroscience, and the design of computer systems.[27]

Granted the cultural prejudice against engineering after 1850, it must be said that the historians of engineering since that date have done well in the field of narrative history. Narrative historians, from Samuel Smiles to L T C Rolt, have achieved a great deal which is admirable and valuable; it is sheer ignorance to assume that they are worthy of only adverse criticism. This 'engineer's history' has suffered, though, through being developed apart from the discipline of academic history, and it is striking that in the Great Britain of 1993, history of engineering is not integrated with history as an academic discipline. This is not all loss. It leaves the way open, unobstructed by those ignorant of science in all its aspects, to develop history of engineering within the discipline of engineering itself, with links thrown out to economics, economic history and philosophy of science, and with close co-operation with the engineering professional institutions and the more enlightened museums.

Many of the authors after 1850 were nineteenth-century engineers, such as C E Stretton,[28] C J Bowen-Cooke[29] or F Trevithick,[30] who provided accurate narratives of the development of the equipment in their branch of engineering. In the twentieth century, examples include E L Ahrons.[31] These works can be added to earlier works by 'natural philosophers' like D Lardner[32] or J Bourne.[33] This is not history according to the interpretation of the philosopher–historians who were gaining in influence, particularly in Germany, after Hegel, but the attempt to provide an accurate account of 'what happened' is an honourable one with a long history.

Eusebius was, in part, trying to do this. But as the history of the history of religion shows, disputes concerning the use of historical narrative and the validity of alternative interpretations or accounts become common when polemic, justification, the search for meaning and the belief that there is a purpose behind events enter the picture. An attempt to chart, for example, the evolution of computers from seventeenth-century origins to the present, following one of the structural patterns for histories laid down by Eusebius, Illyricus, Baronius or G Arnold, will confront the author with such considerations.

This problem had to be faced in religious matters, particularly after the Reformation. By the nineteenth century, the history of religion was a very diverse and rich field, in which methodology, epistemology, historiography and philosophy were interrelated, with simple narrative history scarcely adequate to answer the questions which faced Christianity from the seventeenth century onwards, and which had discredited naive supernaturalism and biblical literalism as fit only for the credulous and the ignorant.[34] In the nineteenth century, it was possible to believe that such questions concerning history, which had first appeared in the field of religious studies, did not concern the historian of engineering, but this can scarcely be argued today. It is worth noting that the several different approaches to history, disputes concerning correct method and the purposes of historical analysis, were never resolved in the context of religion, and there is no likelihood that they will be resolved within the sphere of engineering and industrial studies. All the analyst can do is to understand the several philosophies of history, and guard against uncritical acceptance of any one method to the exclusion of others.

Epistemology within an engineering context; the validity of alternative conclusions drawn from common data; the structure of engineering histories; historicism and engineering progress; socio-political interpretations of engineering; and philosophy of technology are pushing 'history of engineering' and 'history of the history of engineering' into the same complex condition as history of religion and history of the history of religion in the nineteenth century.[35] Yet the problem has hardly been tackled with any success, and the reason is obvious. The pioneers of the history of religion, philosophy of religion, modern biblical criticism and modern theology, by and large understood religion. Many of them were, or had been, ministers or practising members of the Judaeo-Christian group of religions, as well as being historians, philosophers and theologians. Witness Descartes, Pascal, Bayle, Semler, Reimarus, Schliermacher, Strauss, Feuerbach, Kierkegaard, Schweitzer, Bultmann, Tillich, Kung and Cupitt, to name but a few who have shaped modern religious thought over the last 350 years.[36] But the attempt to provide a corresponding body of historic-philosophical analysis for engineering has been done by persons largely without the same degree of understanding of engineering. Many historians who have tackled engineering cannot read an engineering drawing or perform the simplest engineering calculation — unlike the historians and philosophers of the physical sciences and mathematics who are generally most competent in the technicalities of the speciality they study. Ideally, the work should be carried through by engineers themselves. Having been too-often tackled by subscribers to the pure science myth, or sociologists, historians and philosophers who have never been subjected to the discipline of engineering in any way, the attempt has largely failed. It will continue to fail until engineers themselves master the methods of history and philosophy and address this problem. Fortunately the nature of present-day exemplary technology is compelling them to do just this.

Popular engineering history and widespread misconceptions

Before considering present-day history of engineering in the light of the changing nature of strategic technologies, several common misconceptions about engineers, arising from popular history, will be briefly reviewed in what is openly admitted to be a most incomplete survey. I believe that these misconceptions arose because 'history of engineering' has been derived largely by amateur historians through the tradition established in the mid-nineteenth century by Samuel Smiles (often without his competence), or compiled by engineers writing about their profession or their industry, who were joined in the twentieth century by enthusiasts who knew something about engineering equipment, calculations and methods. This is particularly the case with narrative history of the technical equipment itself. No mean-minded disparagement of the pioneers of engineering history is intended, and I acknowledge my debt to the hard-working, thorough, and knowledgeable writers of the history of major areas of engineering apparatus, without which serious analytical history can scarcely begin. The fact that such works steer clear of the speculations found in histories of religion, politics, and pure science is commonly regarded as points in their favour. To those who regard such speculations as pretentious, carefully compiled narrative history is the standard — the norm to be aimed at — but even here there must be some methods of selecting material, lest everything be included without discrimination, and selection demands classification into categories, which demands some analysis according to a system.

Many writers about engineering history, not educated in method, simply assume without question the prevailing prejudices of their class, which in Britain after 1850 included an imprecisely formulated historicism taking the form of a faith in progress, with great men (agents of providence) inventing the essential devices in acts expressive of personal genius and individual enterprise. The myth of the engineer was usually presented with some romantic touches, as if they were a new kind of artist or craftsman, using steel and concrete rather than paints, canvas or wood.[37]

There was a tendency to concentrate on the artefact — the equipment designed — rather than the mental processes which resulted in the design. This omission of a vital element has distorted engineering history and philosophy to the present. The emphasis on individual engineers, with a frequent neglect of their methods, and omissions of references to their assistants and staffs, has distorted the popular conception of British — and world — engineering. The errors have been compounded by the failure to classify the several kinds of engineer and engineering activity in an age which grows impatient of scholarship and which is turning historical studies into a branch of entertainment.

Engineers who are of a kind likely to interest the public, or who personify the popularly perceived 'myth of the engineer', such as I K Brunel, have been given much greater publicity than those who do not, or whose work might demand considerable skills to be understood, such as H Riall Sankey, H E Ives or F W Taylor. Persons with an engineering background, such as the philosophers Herbert Spencer (onetime member of Robert Stephenson's staff of engineers) or L Wittgenstein (aeronautical engineering student) are usually never associated with the discipline in any way.

Popular history is dominated by the post-Newcomen age, with the emphasis on 1740–1940, and too-little account taken of the changes in the nature of technology, before, during, and after that time. Generally there is little effort to relate the engineering changes to socio-political, and economic issues. There are exceptions, but these are too few.

Consider the range of engineering activity, the different kinds of engineer, and the nature of their contributions represented by the following names: H Austin, I K Brunel, M Brunel, V Bush, L Carnot, S Carnot, C Cockroft, T A Edison, H Ford, B Franklin, H L Gantt, H L Le Chatelier, J J Heilmann, Lord Hinton of Bankside, H E Ives, C 'Boss' Kettering, H Lemp, J Leupold, G V Lomonossoff, W Morris, C Polhem, H L Gantt, I Schoenberg, A P Sloan, J Smeaton, F J Sprague, G Stephenson, R Stephenson, F W Taylor, A M Wellington. These could be arranged under the headings of engineer–craftsman; engineer–creator; engineer–inventor; engineer–manager; engineer–organiser; engineer–philosopher; engineer–politician; engineer–scientist; engineer–soldier; and this list of headings is by no means exhaustive. Some engineers, such as Edison, would appear under several headings.

One could examine the part played in an engineer's work by the creative, the derivative, and the synthetic engineering design traditions, but this is seldom done, and many biographies fail to classify an engineer's design method according to any system. Yet this simple classification can yield very fruitful results, identifying those who introduce radically new devices, systems, methods or concepts; those who apply innovations originating elsewhere; and those who effect a synthesis of a range of innovations from several sources. Some famous engineers, such as Sir Nigel Gresley, the Chief Mechanical Engineer of the London North Eastern Railway Co., created little, but applied, with great discrimination and judgement, the innovations of others.[38] Ford worked in all three traditions, as do all great engineers to some extent.[39]

The recognised contribution of individual engineers in history is often limited by the public's ability to comprehend what they have done. The engineers described by Smiles typified, and still typify, the kind of engineer whose life and work is readily comprehended by the general public. They are furthermore the kind of engineers liked by the organisers of programmes for the media and for museum exhibitions, by school teachers, and by authors of popular works. Things are changing, as more people gain an understanding of electronics, and as societies develop which specialise in history of electronics, computing and post-World War Two technology, but for every person who can read about the works of Brunel, George Stephenson or Gresley with some comprehension, there are fewer who can appreciate the work of A D Blumlein (electronics), E F Alexanderson (poly-phase motors) or any of the great electrical engineers. Even where the author tries to avoid technicalities, it is much more difficult to give the general public an understanding of representative twentieth-century technology, like electronics or electrical systems, than it is to describe the basics of eighteenth-century strategic engineering.

The popular conception of engineers and their work is limited by the popular understanding of engineering. This is often wrong, and the general public may overrate its understanding, but the man in the street probably grasps the principles of the Newcomen steam engine to a greater extent than he does the principles of a bridge circuit for measuring cell impedance. He would not understand the thermodynamics of the Newcomen steam engine, as demonstrated by Sankey or I Kolin, with the aid of the temperature–entropy diagram, but he understands enough to grasp some of the working of this machine, and to comprehend its significance. But he does not get anything like as far with the basic principles of pneumatic control systems, inverter control of three-phase motors, radio-broadcasting, or other technologies which have come to typify best practice in the twentieth century. Nor does the school teacher, or the average museum visitor — which is why a phrase such as 'great British engineer' conjures up an image of a nineteenth-century figure (probably Brunel standing by the *Great Eastern* launching chains) rather than Blumlein. Brunel fits preconceived notions of what an engineer should be, in the 'great man' or 'romantic' tradition, whereas it is difficult to get a simple picture of the achievements of Sankey, Schoenberg, G Kron or S P Thompson. Some extremely important engineers do not have lives which can be romanticised for public consumption, and the only way to understand what they have done is to read their collected papers. This applies to a man like H E Ives who spent most of his life in the Bell telephone laboratories.[40] Even where the mass media have romanticised a great engineer's life (Alexander Bell, Thomas Edison), a balanced view of his achievements demands a study of his work to a depth, and with a breadth beyond the application of the general reader. Hence the misconceptions persist. For every thousand people who know (a grossly simplified account) of Bell and the telephone, how many know of his contributions to the theory of space frames, hydroplanes and work with the deaf and dumb?[41] How many know of Edison's method for analysing and developing heavy-current electrical systems?

In Britain, the romanticising of the inventor ('the boffin') by absurd films, television programmes, popular books and magazines has reinforced the image of the isolated individual at work, and deflected popular attention from the team worker, or the great organiser (like Schoenberg, Lord Weir, Lord Ashfield, General Groves, Bush). The greatest of engineers can be overlooked. Lomonossoff and Wellington were amongst the very first analysts to create mathematical models of industrial systems set in an economic context. Both analysed the railway system and its economic and geophysical 'receiving system', Wellington in the USA from the 1880s onwards, Lomonossoff in Russia, Germany and Britain from the 1890s onwards. Their work is of supreme importance in the history of applied mathematics and economic theory, yet they are scarcely known outside specialists working in the field of railway economics and analysis of traction. It is not just the technical difficulty of their work which is responsible for this. Albert Einstein is known. Nikolai Lobatchevski is known. János Bolyai is known. Alfred Newton is known. It is that the cultural prejudices reviewed earlier in the paper have caused engineering matters, and economic analysis, to rate below pure mathematics, geometry and physics in the interests of those competent to deal with these matters and able to bring them before the public.

Even engineers associated with technologies which the public can understand to some extent receive less than their due. In twentieth-century Britain, best engineering practice is represented by Austin, Morris or F Whittle, rather than by Gresley or O V S Bulleid, yet the locomotive engineers receive a much greater public acclaim from people who owe more to the motor car and jet aeroplane than they do to the steam locomotive. J L Baird, with his mechanical and electro-mechanical optical (television) systems is well known in Britain, but how many know of Zworykin, Nipkow, Ives or A A Campbell Swinton? W von Braun is known in connection with the development of the heavy-duty rocket, but how many persons could name equally important contributors to the German programme, such as General Dornberger? Charles Parsons and the steam turbine are known, but what of G de Laval, or A Stodola? Rudolf Diesel is known, but what of his associate R Pawlikowski who worked on the coal-fired diesel between 1911 and 1944, or Diesel's close friends, the Brunlers, who developed combustion with the flames submerged in contact with the water?

Clearly the pernicious influence of 'history' corrupted by petty nationalism, racism, or political ideology, which has blighted too much so-called history is partly responsible here. 'Great-man history' has encouraged the uncritical public to look for 'the one' who is responsible for a particular innovation rather than the many. The squabbling about priorities, which was so common in the seventeenth and eighteenth centuries, still found although to a lesser extent, coupled with puerile nationalistic prejudices, led to a ready acceptance of simplified history of innovation, which is the only history of technology encountered by a sizeable proportion of the masses.

Obviously, there is a tendency to concentrate on those successful innovations which became current, or which though failures, stimulated research which eventually led to success, but a more scholarly, systematic history would review the failures (Pawlikowski, O Brunler) and assess the successes more critically. It would also outline engineering method, and relate changes in the nature of engineering to changes in the socio-economic 'receiving system'.

Difficulties are readily admitted. The growth of huge international corporations, maintaining large research and development teams, means that vital, original contributions are made by teams, or members of teams about whom it is difficult for outsiders to learn. Military or commercial secrecy place restrictions on publicising what goes on, or what went on, in the research establishments which created much of the strategic technology of the twentieth century. Certainly one reason why Blumlein remained relatively unknown to all but his colleagues was that his work remained internal to the research establishment where he made so many of his fundamental contributions to electronics during the 1939–1945 war. It was not published, and it was subject to military security after his death in an aeroplane accident during the war. The work of Professor R Burns in giving Blumlein his belated due is very much to be applauded.[42] Many great engineers published relatively little, and the public know nothing of their endeavours because the internal company documents, or the consultants' reports through which their ideas took effect are never encountered.

Many great engineers have been overlooked by both the public and historians. There is Sankey, who pioneered systematic testing of industrial heat engines between 1890 and 1910, and who developed practical methods for applying thermodynamical analysis to all kinds of prime mover. There is W S Durtnall, the advocate of thermal-electric systems who worked with J J Heilmann in exploring the form electric railways should take, and who helped introduce steam-electric ships, oil-electric ships, and locomotives and road-cars with electric transmission. He was very active between 1890 and 1930 and a regular contributor to the professional institutions, yet historians have ignored him.

A scholarly history of technology could be devised by starting with engineering design theory, and philosophy of technology as defined by engineers to give a definition of engineering method. Innovation analysis supplies definitions of the several 'levels' of engineering activity found at any one time in one area, and suggests ways of classifying the ideal phases through which technologies pass from innovation to obsolescence. Econometrics suggests methods for grading particular technologies in order of influence in the global economy, and for classifying the major stages of economic growth and the part played by engineering in causing them. Integrating these methods should give history of engineering the philosophy and methods which it needs.

Clearly it will be the work of years to carry through this integration, and to demonstrate it via case studies, although my own work in the field of railway traction has met with encouraging success. Using this kind of history as a basis for popular accounts of engineering change, which ideally should be written by the same scholars who are creating the mature history, should go some way to removing the popular misconceptions concerning engineering and engineers which plague Great Britain today.

In the heads of school children, teachers, and the general public, these misconceptions are bad enough, but in the heads of politicians, civil servants, university chancellors and — let it be admitted — engineers themselves, they are dangerous. They retard the economic development of Great Britain, they hinder the growth of the engineering profession, they malign a vital cultural activity and they perpetuate a harmful error. It is time this error was corrected.

A suggested outline for a systematic, analytical history of technology

General statements about the nature of engineering should come first. Engineering has never had a general theory concerning its nature and, in the past, historical studies of it have grown piecemeal, resulting in an eclectic, imperfectly integrated collection of particular studies. The attempts to form general theories of the nature of engineering and of its history have been done without understanding of engineering by non-engineers, and they have failed.

Several aspects must be taken into account. In any period, in any place, there exist alongside each other engineering systems and artefacts of different kinds. Engineering changes in nature, and it is changing radically at the present time. These different kinds of engineering entity originated in different ages and cultures, and they are associated with very different methods, concepts and traditions. Distinguishing between these different kinds of engineering, and charting their histories is essential.[43]

In any one age, some engineering systems and practices are much more important than others. In papers published elsewhere, I have defined strategic technologies as those which set the standard for defining what is meant by 'modern technology' during a particular period.[44] Groups of strategic technologies (always relatively few in number) combine to form the engineering bases for those industries — again few in number — which dominate the global economy, and which are responsible for distinct phases of economic growth. The econometricians S Kuznets, J A Schumpeter and G Mensch have examined the role of industry, and innovation within the context of economic growth.[45]

The water frame, the spinning jenny, the carding engine, the Crompton mule, the Newcomen steam engine, the Watt steam engine, the Cornish engine are obvious examples of engineering entities of strategic importance underlying the strategic industries of the eighteenth century — textiles, iron making, coal mining. The high-pressure steam engine, the marine engine, the Scotch boiler likewise made steam navigation possible. The steam locomotive, the electric telegraph, the technology for producing steel in bulk, and the civil engineering methods (many cultivated in the canal building era) brought into existence the steam railway which served as exemplar for heavy industry down to 1890. These technologies, and the wide-ranging industries dependent on them, have been fairly well explored by historians, and the public conception of engineer and engineering is often formed by works dealing with the period 1700–1890, if not written during this time.

But the strategic technologies, and industries before 1700 and after 1890 were different in nature. The introduction of heavy-duty electrotechnology as exemplar marked a change in the nature of the exemplar, as the mechanical exemplar was replaced by an electrical one. Throughout the twentieth century, the change in the nature of technology is marked by the change in the technology which represents engineering at its most advanced. The German chemical manufacturing industry, the American automotive industry, aviation, electronics, nuclear engineering, microelectronics, information technology, and now in 1993 the technology associated with advanced investigations into perception, neuroscience, and genetics represent quickening stages in this evolution.

The engineer representative of each stage sometimes differs in philosophy, methods, conceptual apparatus, education and standards from the engineer in a contemporary branch of engineering which is no longer exemplary–strategic, or from an engineer working in a strategic technology in a former age. To chart these differences and — equally important — to note the similarities, are vitally important, and analysts of engineering change must pay greater attention to them.

A greater degree of research and development work took place within great combines, or government establishments after 1890. Witness the work of Edison, Edison-General Electric, General Motors, Marconi, EMI, and the state-controlled military industrial complexes of the wartime period and after. The development of radar, the V2 rocket, the atomic bomb, the proximity fuse, the inter-continental ballistic missile, the advanced electronics needed for modern military systems, bacteriological and chemical weapons, code-breaking technology — these are but a few examples of engineering devices and systems radically different from the strategic, exemplary systems of earlier ages like the water wheels at London Bridge or Marly, or the great wind-organs of the medieval cathedrals, or the weight-driven clocks of the thirteenth and fourteenth centuries, or the capital ships of the Victorian and Edwardian navies.

What are the differences, and the similarities, with respect to their engineering method, between a Ramelli, a Smeaton, a Newcomen, a Telford, a Brunel, an Edison, a Marconi, a Prandtl, a Blumlein, a Brattain, a von Braun, a Turing, a Cockroft, a Lord Hinton? Organisations became bigger and more complex, and the specialist engineer–organisers, the great co-ordinators of teams who liaise with government, financial institutions and other industries retain the importance they had in the sixteenth century, but they sometimes have remained in the background, or obscured in the bureaucracy of the military–industrial complex, misunderstood by the public. What are the similarities and differences between C Polhem, George Stephenson, J D Rockefeller, A P Sloan, A Speer, F de Lesseps, General G W Goethals, Viscount Weir, General L Groves, or Vannevar Bush?

Clearly, the analysis of industrial and company organisation is needed here, but one needs to investigate the contributions made by particular individuals to evolving engineering method and conceptual apparatus. Engineering is primarily a matter of mind, as it is from ideas that the devices are born, not from a previous generation of devices. What goes on in the designer's head is the really important part, yet the psychology of engineering innovation needs to be formulated: it has hardly begun to be developed. A good, systematic analysis of theories of innovation, design and formulations of engineering method can contribute much.[46] Note should be taken of those engineers who built up theory and conceptual apparatus — Castigliano, Carnot, Bernoulli, Fessenden, Turing.

Engineering design is basically the creation in the imagination of idealised constructs which are then realised, and integrated in existing engineering systems of varying degrees of modernity, which are themselves integrated with a larger socio-political 'receiving system'. Integrating the innovation into the system, and integrating the system with the general 'receiving system' is an essential skill, one of the greatest of all engineering skills. It is the mark of the strategic thinker, the valuable possession of the engineering manager and organiser. Identifying engineers who have acted in this role, in wartime, or in a large-scale project (such as the US Apollo project) would help redress a balance which has been too much upset in favour of the engineer–inventor as conceived in the period 1700–1890.

Qualitative life history of technology splits the idealised life of a technology into isolated endeavour: first formulation of prototype, selection of successful archetype, stage of improvement by incorporation of incremental innovation, emergence of classical form, approach to obsolescence via pseudo-innovations, 'design impasse' and obsolescence.[47] Certain engineers have a gift for making a contribution during one particular phase of a particular technology. Others make contributions across the full life history.

Economic history, and methods for assessing the wealth generated by particular industries, should be noted. Insight into the importance of industries, and the technologies on which they depend, can be gained by looking at the economists' listing of major industries in order of the increase they contribute to investments, or to gross national product.

These methods can help sort out the major, significant industries and their technologies from the less important, and help direct the attention of the historian to those engineers — who fall into several categories — who create these technologies, and manage and organise them. The people likely to do this job best are engineers with industrial experience working with other engineers who have mastered the methods of historical analysis. Engineers will need to work with economists, econometricians and analysts of those aspects of the 'receiving system' into which engineering creations, and dependent industries, must fit with sufficient harmony to function. Engineers can learn much from those who have provided accurate histories of engineering-based industries, or of engineering institutions, or of engineering education. This does not mean, however, that a sound exercise in the history of institutions, or of education, or sociology, or economics is history of engineering. Too many 'externalists' pass off work coming under these headings as if it were history of engineering itself. This must be resisted on the grounds of accuracy.

There are as many errors to be corrected by engineers concerning the history of engineering as perceived by historians, as there are errors to be corrected by engineers concerning the natures of engineering and the engineer.

Notes and references

1 Marwick, A, *The Nature of History* (London: Macmillan, 1976)

2 Duffy, M C, 'Evolution of engineering design technique', *Engineering Designer* (Jan/Feb 1979), pp19–22; (Mar/Apr 1979), pp19–22; (May/June 1979), pp21–26; (July/Aug), pp31–35; (Sept/Oct), pp19–23; (Nov/Dec), pp21–26

3 Marwick, A, makes only passing mention to history of technology, or engineering.

4 Problems confronting the historian of technology are reviewed by several authors in 'The Newcomen Society Diamond Jubilee', *Transactions of the Newcomen Society*, 51 (1979–1980), pp193–228.

5 Wilken, R, *The Myth of Christian Beginnings* (London: SCM Press, 1979); Butterfield, H, *Writing on Christianity and History* (Oxford: Oxford University Press, 1979)

6 For example, Singer *et al.* (eds), *A History of Technology* (Oxford: Oxford University Press, 1958). *The Oxford History of England* (Oxford: Clarendon Press), splits its subject into centuries or distinct epochs, and examines themes within each epoch.

7 For example, Krantzberg, M and Pursell, C (eds), *Technology in Western Civilisation* (Oxford: Oxford University Press, 1967)

8 Dircks, H, *Perpetuum Mobile* (London: Spon, 1861)

9 Klemm, F, *A History of Western Technology* (London: George Allen & Unwin, 1959); Wolf, A, *A History of Science, Technology and Philosophy in the 16th and 17th Centuries* (London: George Allen & Unwin, 1935, 1968); Butterfield, H, *Origins of Modern Science* (London: G Bell & Sons, 1957)

10 Bronowski, J and Mazlish, B, *The Western Intellectual Tradition from Leonardo to Hegel* (London: Hutchinson, 1960); Cupitt, D, *Sea of Faith* (London: BBC Books, 1986)

11 Dijksterhuis, E J, *The Mechanisation of the World Picture* (London: Oxford University Press, 1961)

12 Rational and scientific management of entire nations along the lines of 'Taylorised' industry was advocated by the American Technocracy movement, described by Akin, W E, *Technocracy and the American Dream; the Technocrat Movement 1900–1941* (Berkeley: University of California Press, 1977). See also Urwick, L and Brech, E F L, *The Making of Scientific Management* (London: Pitman, 1951, 1953)

13 Keller, A G, *A Theatre of Machines* (London: Chapman Hall, 1964)

14 Pollard, S, *The Idea of Progress* (London: Pelican, 1971). The idea of progress in all activities became increasingly common. See Bronowski J and Mazlish, B; Wolf, A.

15 Mure, G R G, *The Philosophy of Hegel* (London: Oxford University Press, 1965); Kung, H, *Does God Exist?* (London: Collins, 1980)

16 Camus, A, *The Rebel* (London: Penguin, 1951, 1971)

17 Popper, K, *The Poverty of Historicism* (London: Routledge, 1986)

18 Carlyle, T, *On Heroes and Hero-worship and the Heroic in History* (London: Oxford University Press, 1904 edn)

19 Collingwood, R G, *The Idea of History* (London: Oxford University Press, 1961); Butterfield, H, *Origins of History* (London: Eyre Methuen, 1981), *Man on his Past*

(Cambridge: Cambridge University Press, 1969)
20 Smiles, S, *The Lives of the Engineers* (London: Murray, 1861; Newton Abbot: David & Charles, 1968)
21 Wiener, M J, *English Culture and the Decline of the Industrial Spirit 1850–1980* (Cambridge: Cambridge University Press, 1981), p28
22 Barnett, C, *Audit of War* (London: Macmillan, 1986)
23 Wiener, M J, p28
24 Arnold, M, *Culture and Anarchy* (Cambridge: Cambridge University Press, 1869, 1971); Newman, J H, *Idea of a University* (London: Rinehart & Winston Holt, 1960 edn); Snow, C P, *The Two Cultures and a Second Look* (Cambridge: Cambridge University Press, 1962)
25 Twain, M, *A Connecticut Yankee in King Arthur's Court* (London: Macmillan, 1889)
26 Cardwell, D S L, *From Watt to Clausius* (London: Heinemann, 1971): exemplary study of engineering practice directly generating a science (thermodynamics).
27 Churchland, P M, *Matter and Consciousness* (Cambridge, MA: Bradford-MIT Press, 1984, 1988)
28 Stretton, C E, *Development of the Locomotive: a Popular History 1803–1903* (London: Crosby Lockwood, 1903)
29 Bowen-Cooke, C J, *British Locomotives* (London: Whittaker & Co., 1894)
30 Trevithick, F, *Life of Richard Trevithick, with an Account of his Inventions* (London: Spon, 1872)
31 Ahrons, E L, *The British Steam Railway Locomotive 1825–1925* (London: Locomotive Publishing Co., 1925)
32 Lardner, D, *The Steam Engine* (London: John Taylor, 1827, 1836)
33 Bourne, J, *A Treatise on the Steam Engine in its Application to Mines, Mills, Steam Navigation and Railways* (London: Longman Brown Green Longman, 1846)
34 Cupitt, D
35 Philosophy of technology is essential here. A start has been made by Rapp, F, *Analytical Philosophy of Technology* (Dordrecht: D Reidel, 1981). Schuurman, E, *Technology and the Future: a Philosophical Challenge* (Toronto: Wedge Publishing Foundation, 1980)
36 Cupitt, D
37 The role of craft knowledge in engineering science is discussed by Carlson, W B, 'Building Thomas Edison's laboratory at West Orange, New Jersey: a case study in using craft knowledge for technological invention 1886–1888', *History of Technology*, 13 (1991), pp150–67.
38 Brown, F A S, *Nigel Gresley* (London: Ian Allan, 1961, 1975)
39 Jardim, A, *The First Henry Ford: a Study in Personality and Business Leadership* (Cambridge MA: MIT Press, 1970)
40 Burns, R W, 'The contributions of the Bell Telephone Laboratories to the early development of television', *History of Technology*, 13 (1991) pp181–213
41 Bruce, R V, *Bell: Alexander Graham Bell and the Conquest of Solitude* (London: Gollancz, 1973)
42 Burns, R W, Lynch, A C, Lodge, J A, White, E L C, Thrower, K R and Trim, R M, 'The life & work of A D Blumlein', *Engineering Science & Education Journal* (June 1993), pp115–36: edited papers from IEE meeting, 26 October 1992, IEE London
43 Duffy, M C, 'Evolution of engineering design technique'
44 Duffy, M C, 'Technomorphology, innovation and energy analysis: concepts and perspective', *Journal of Mechanical Working Technology*, 7 (1982/1983), pp233–67
45 Kuznets, S, *Economic Change* (New York: Norton & Co., 1953); Kuznets, S, *Economic Growth and Structure* (New York: Norton & Co., 1965); Kuznets, S, *Economic Growth of Nations* (Cambridge, MA: Harvard University Press, 1971); Mensch, G, *Stalemate in Technology: Innovations Overcome the Depression* (Cambridge MA: Ballinger, 1979); Schumpeter, J A, *Konjunkturzyklen II* (Gottingen: 1961)
46 Hubka, V, *Principles of Engineering Design* (Zurich: Goldach, 1980; Oxford: Butterworth Scientific, 1982): methodological procedures of design. Usher, A P, *History of Mechanical Inventions* (Cambridge, MA: Harvard University Press, 1929) opens with discussion of the nature of the innovative process.
47 Duffy, M C, 'Evolution of engineering design technique', 'Technomorphology, innovation and energy analysis'; Foster, R, *Innovation: the Attacker's Advantage* (London: Macmillan, 1986)

Index

This index covers personal and company names, constructions and major primary sources. Endnotes are referenced if they provide additional textual information. *n* refers to endnotes, qualified by the endnote number in parentheses and *Pl* refers to plates.